PEOPLE!

Woe unto them that join house to house,
that lay field to field, till there be no place,
that they may be placed alone in the midst
of the earth!

Isaiah. Chapter V, 8

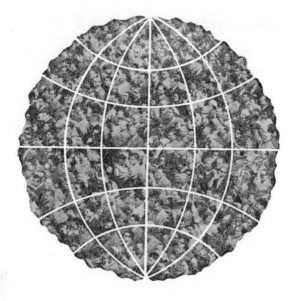

CHALLENGE TO SURVIVAL

author of ROAD TO SURVIVAL

WILLIAM SLOANE ASSOCIATES
New York   1960

Grateful acknowledgment is made to the American Association for the Advancement of Science for permission to reprint material from "A Medical Aspect of the Population Problem," by Alan Gregg, published in *Science* for May 13, 1960, and to The Tuttle Company for permission to reprint material from *The Japanese Are Like That*, by Ichiro Kawasaki.

Published simultaneously in the Dominion of Canada by George J. McLeod Limited, Toronto.

Printed in the United States of America.

Library of Congress Catalog Card Number 60–13347

To the volunteer and staff workers for birth control

Their far-sighted and selfless dedication, often in the face of intolerance and even persecution, has helped to create both practical methods and a climate of understanding that bring nearer by decades the possibility of halting runaway population growth. We may thus hope to escape catastrophe that— without their labors—would have been a virtual certainty.

Contents

Foreword

The background for this book is, in part, travel in more than twenty-five countries on four continents and in forty-nine of our fifty states.

So far as possible capital cities and large towns were avoided, and every opportunity was taken to learn as much as possible about geography, land use, agriculture, forestry, conservation, and the attitudes of people toward land and water, and the products they draw from them.

This book deals with the most fateful problem of our day, excessive population growth. Every man, woman and child in the world is feeling its pressure one way or another. Unless effective action—now not even in sight—is taken to solve it, it could result in a particularly grim form of death for millions, and the end of civilization as we know it.

Industrialization has been expanding rapidly, though in many parts of the world it has not begun to catch up with population growth. And the people of even the most highly industrialized country depend on the land for food, water, and a host of other raw materials that feed the maw of the machine. There has seemed to be a tendency to overlook this, on the part of those concerned with "developing" the non-industrialized parts of the world. Even in the United States, over half of the raw material used by industry comes from the ranch, farm or forest.

From the up-and-down fields of Honshu and the Urubamba Valley, to the plains of the Deccan and Patagonia, and the Lofoten fishing grounds, man has swarmed over the earth and responded in an incalculable number of ways to the myriad combinations of conditions he has encountered. These are of endless fascination.

The understanding of nature's laws, evolved by a tiny minority of the human race, and applied to ends both constructive and destructive, is impressive. But this understanding is, unfortunately, restricted to a miniscule proportion of the nearly three billion people in the world. And some of the most brilliant insights are given to such small fractions of even the well-informed that understanding them has limited or often non-existent influence. Much human behavior, including thinking, has advanced but little beyond that of Cro-Magnon man. Astrologers hold high status in India (illiteracy rate, 80 per cent) and syndicate their writings widely in the press of the United States (illiteracy rate, 2 per cent). Because most of us are ignoring the working of nature's laws, men, women and children are in trouble, and enduring very grievous suffering indeed, in much of the world. Unless there is a major extension and revision of most important knowledge and the best thinking, far greater suffering lies ahead—and not very far ahead, at that.

There are vast differences among the thousands of millions of men, women and children, but we also share many qualities. We may enjoy different things; practically all of us have a great capacity for happiness. Some of us have been conditioned toward a brave stoicism, but there is probably not a very wide difference in our nerve endings, and the pangs of hunger do not vary much from the Punjab to Ceará. The youngsters at the soda fountain in Des Moines may have little awareness of the family crowded into the hovel in Hong Kong, but every one of us should remember that, "There, but for the grace of God—"

By a special and largely fortuitous combination of circumstances we Americans have been able to reach a level of material comfort without precedent in the history of the world. This most of us have identified with a penultimate, if not an ultimate, good, and with the zeal of dedicated missionaries we are making at least the gesture of extending it to the rest of the world.

As we succeed in greater or lesser degree in "raising living standards" we unquestionably raise hell with the *status quo ante*, and the way of life of hundreds of millions of men, women and children—not to mention their indispensable habitat. We are, it seems to me after nearly a decade in "underdeveloped" countries, extraordinarily uncritical of both our aims and accomplishments. One of my hopes, in writing this book, is to raise some doubts about our impact on other people's lives. Although I am neither a demographer nor a sociologist, years of observation of people in varied cultures and habitats have given me unusual opportunities to watch many kinds of human beings travel from diverse pasts toward futures that are increasingly fouled-up by excessive crowding. What is happening to them is not very different from the experiences of other forms of life under comparable circumstances.

We have been liberally dosed, during the past decade or two, with clichés as to the impossibility of continuing prosperous existence "in a sea of poverty," though this has been the way of the world for thousands of generations. We must, we are told, protect the sources of raw materials that are the very basis of our economy—and in the next breath we are told we need not worry about running out of raw materials since "science" will find substitutes.

We need, I think, apologize not at all for trying to maintain a high standard of living in America, though many of us wish there might be more emphasis on quality than quantity. It is only because we have a high living standard that we have been able to give as much help as we have to our fellow man.

Harvard's success in raising $82,000,000 for its endowment should be a cause of gratification for the whole world. For it is from the classrooms and laboratories of our universities that many of America's gifts to the world come.

On the other hand, it is hard not to remember the hundreds of millions who live with pain, cold, rags and hunger. It would be an unusual American, indeed, who did not want to help. He would certainly not want to extend the pool of deprivation. Yet, in some parts of the earth, this seems to be the real effect of our efforts. And later consequences of our behavior may well be to drag down the living standards of ourselves, surely of our children.

It is these conclusions, and the observations and data (not all, by any means, original with me) on which the conclusions are based, that make up the body of this book. If, sometimes, the drama of the situations in which these people exist is set forth, this is done because the drama is there—and in the hope it will help the reader appreciate the feelings shared by many of the world's millions.

Little is said, here, about resources and their conservation since these subjects were discussed at length in a book published twelve years ago. The small amount of localized conservation progress during the ensuing period has been more than offset by greater resource abuse in most of the world, and even more by the growth of human demands and increasingly destructive technology.

Statistics are rounded, in part because even those from official sources are apt to show some failure of agreement, and in part because there are significant changes from month to month.

This is a personal essay and a personal assay. It cannot be too strongly emphasized that the conclusions and points of view are my own and not those of Planned Parenthood organizations. These are made up of a diversity of people, with refreshingly varied points of view, and I am sure that I shall encounter among them some of the most vigorous dissents from my values and findings. A host of matters are here discussed on which Planned Parenthood has not taken a formal position. Nor should it.

My debts to those who have helped in field work and otherwise are so many I cannot possibly mention them all; indeed, some of them have taught me without giving me their names. Special thanks are due, however, to the John Simon Guggenheim Memorial Foundation which, along with a Fulbright Fellowship, made it possible for me to live and travel extensively almost a year in Norway, Denmark and Sweden. The Conservation Foundation also helped with a travel grant. The embassies and information offices of the three Scandinavian countries were unstinting with their cooperation. Particularly helpful, also, were Frøken Hélène Hertzberg, Th. Rasmussen, Nils Dahlbeck and the late Anders Fjelstad. Ornithologists, amateur and professional, around the world have made me part of their freemasonry and given me not only the pleasure of knowing their birds but of seeing their countries through the eyes of trained naturalists and ecologists. Social and natural scientists, government officials, farmers, fishermen, businessmen—and many others—have been more than kind to a willing listener. None of those named or un-named is, of course, responsible for errors in the text. Authors and publishers who have given permission to quote are named.

The reader may, at times, detect a seeming ambivalence—or polyvalence—both in judgments of situations and the possibilities of coping with them. There is often no possible simple analysis, nor simple resolution, of problems. Much will often, or always, depend on a given situation at a given time. Certain steps that are here urged seem to me, after not inconsiderable experience, to be indispensable. The difficulty may often lie not so much with the things we do as with those left undone. The pooling of experience and knowledge is most urgently needed—the widest and best experience and knowledge that can be marshalled. Yet "Do nothing," is the policy of most governments, and of the U.N. and associated agencies, with reference to excessive population growth. It is, in August 1960, still the expressed policy of the United States government.

This situation is one we may expect to change *only* through individual action welded into effective social and political pressure. If this book helps to bring such action about, the work that has gone into it will have been worth while.

W. V.

The Bear Patch
Palenville, N. Y.

PEOPLE!

1

Thunder Overhead

HE WAS AS BROWN AND WRINKLED AS AN OLD BLADDER, and there was about him something of the same collapsed look. His gray beard was scraggly and his clothes were liberally mended. He had the same body odor—not so unpleasant as we hygienic Westerners expect—as many of the world's unwashed I have encountered. He might have been anything from forty to seventy; when you live in an Indian village, you are likely to age early and, like our ancestors of Benjamin Franklin's day, you must possess an innate toughness to survive at all. There were laughter wrinkles running backward from his eyes, and in them a sparkle that in a man of lesser dignity I would have called merry. His bearing and the attitude of the other villagers toward him marked a man of consequence.

"What," I asked him through the interpreter, "is the greatest change that has come to India in your memory?"

Without a pause for thought he answered, with obvious pride, "Independence."

"And what is the next greatest thing?"

He turned to my companion, an American public-health specialist, and replied, "The coming of the doctors." He was so patently sincere that I was sure he was not making the statement out of politeness or a desire to flatter this doctor. For him, it was the simple truth.

"Of course," he added, "when I was a boy we often had three meals a day. Now there are more mouths to fill and we do not always eat twice." Again a simple statement of fact with, so far as I could tell, no hint of complaint or irony. As I looked beyond him to the little mud huts, the sun-baked rice paddies, the gray, sterile-looking soil, I had a clue to the connection between his two statements.

I did not pursue the obvious which, I am sure, he understood as well as I. Unless a near miracle should happen, within ten or fifteen years the people of the village would have even less to eat. I wondered what his eyes would look like then.

The old man, old at forty or seventy, whatever his age might be, could not know that his statements would be quoted around the world; and that it might be ten or fifteen years before most people understood them, and then only after the words had been given an unnecessarily tragic emphasis.

Another conversation, equally meaningful, took place in a New York club, the rich beauty of which also has a message for the man with a sense of history, for it is not likely ever to be equaled again. Like the creations of the de Medicis, it was made possible by the concentration of such wealth as has now been "leveled" down.

My guest was one of my favorite South American friends.

He is a millionaire, a graduate of European universities, a quiet man of notable cultural accomplishments and, what is rarer in Latin America, the possessor of a strong sense of social responsibility. There is no such thing as a "Welfare State" in Latin America (with the possible exception of Uruguay) but Pepe has taken upon himself the responsibility for the welfare of his hundreds of employees. He is sensitive, generous and the possessor of genius for consideration of others. He would be an outstanding citizen, wherever he lived.

He is also troubled. "I can't help thinking," he said, "about the future of my boys." There are three of them, as engaging a trio as one is likely to encounter, with more than a little of the *hidalgoismo* of their father. All three are being educated in the United States.

"The future looks black—very black. [A strong statement for Pepe!] We have made a good deal of progress but not nearly enough. We have started several factories since the last time you visited me, and we keep pegging away at conservation education. We've made a good deal of progress, if you look at it simply in terms of what we have accomplished. But in terms of what is needed, we have done very little. Every year there are more hungry people—or more of our people are hungry. We have tripled our budget for education, but every year there are more people who cannot read or write. Those who get an education, even in our universities, are so half-baked that I sometimes think they would be better off if they were not exposed to books they cannot understand.

"We are a poor country, as you know, and when we have to import our raw materials, it is hard for our little industries to compete in world markets, even when our labor costs are low. Our only real resource is cheap labor and there is growing agitation to raise wages, which means curtailing our only abundant natural resource. You can't blame a man with four, or five, or eight children for wanting more money; our income is still not much over $150 a head, per year. But people don't see that it's better to have a few golden eggs than none at all.

"There is a good deal of discontent and agitation. I don't think there are many Communists. But some other kind of demagogue can be almost as dangerous. And we are setting the stage for trouble.

"Our population is growing 3½ per cent a year and will probably double before 1980—even with the spreading malnutrition. I don't know how we are going to find jobs for all these young people. We are underemployed, now.

"I think a good deal about whether I shouldn't move my family to the States, permanently. It's a big decision to make."

Pepe is obviously deeply concerned. He has a strong sense of responsibility toward his people and also toward his family. He is a man of action and a realist. I should not be surprised to hear, at any time, that he had left South America. If he does, it will be our gain; but it will also be a great loss for his country which can ill afford it.

                                  .

My new friend was a South African girl, a Jewess, who could look with a certain degree of detachment on Boers, Bantu, and British. This was a number of years ago, before Dr. Strijdom, the doctrine of *apartheid*, the Mau-Mau, or the rivers of blood on the Algerian plain.

"It's a mad country," she said, in her lovely voice, completely free of provincial twang. "Quite mad. There's only one way it can end up—in a bloody massacre. And I'm not using 'bloody' in the English sense."

She went on to tell a story illustrative of the tension that even then tautened nerves in the Cape Colony.

A Capetown equivalent of the American country club was having a New Year's Eve party. Spirits of all kinds were running high and everyone was feeling very gay about the new year when into the ballroom leaped a six-foot warrior, nearly naked, armed with a shining spear. He jumped onto the bandstand with a yell. Four women fainted and there were surges toward and away from him.

One of the Englishmen jumped onto the stand and yelled, "It's all right! It's only Gerry." Gerry was one of the young bloods, with a flair for acting and make-up.

"He could easily have been shot," said my friend, "if some of the men hadn't known he was going to do it. It was a fool thing. But he'd started drinking early and thought he'd give them something to remember. And he did. There probably wasn't a man or woman in that room who didn't think for a few seconds, 'This is the beginning.' When you're outnumbered four to one and try to act as though *you* controlled the situation, you can't get away with it forever. Especially when *they* are outbreeding you faster every year.

"It's bound to end in a blood bath, and that won't settle anything."

.

Anna shuddered as the whiplash of the cold northwest wind cut through her thin coat. Sooty ice lined the gutters, and soot covered the cars along both sides of the street. When the bus finally arrived, she was barely able to force her way inside, but in spite of the crush she was grateful for the smelly warmth.

Nothing really got through her consciousness this morning. The stunning impact of yesterday still left her numb. She did not think of the future or even much of the present. Those two hours in the police station had seemed to stretch through the rest of the night into the cold morning. Would they ever end?

Jaime in the *cárcel!* The *policía* had not been unkind to Anna, but they had taken the boy away in the van. He had, they told her, killed another boy with a knife. Jaime, her oldest, and the one she had counted on after Pedro disappeared.

When she had told Pedro she was pregnant for the sixth

time, she thought he was going to beat her up. "Five kids now in this one room with us!" he had shouted, as though it had all been her fault. There was no sunlight and little air. In winter they were cold and in summer there was such heat as San Juan never knew. They couldn't chase the kids out to play as they did at home. And Anna had to work. Pedro's sixty dollars a week wouldn't even buy beans and plantains.

Pedro started staying out at night. He gave her less money. And then, one day, he simply wasn't there. She had known it would happen. This was how it was with other women she knew. She didn't try to find him. She knew he wasn't sick or in an accident. She had known he would go. Maybe he'd gone back to sea.

Many times she had thought of returning to Puerto Rico. But New York was the place of opportunity. This was where the best Puerto Ricans came. Here they could find jobs. Maybe Jaime. . . .

And now Jaime was in trouble, bad trouble.

She didn't know what to do. But she knew she would need money. You always needed money. They had told her they would let her know where Jaime was, help her get a lawyer.

The only thing she could do was to go on working.

                                    .

I was to leave Stockholm the next morning and our farewell party had gone on for some time at one of the city's good restaurants, which is to say one of the best in the world. There had been much genial *skåling*, followed by downing small glasses of excellent Skåne *aquavit* with light beer chasers. By eleven o'clock I had had enough but my hosts insisted that the evening was just getting under way.

"Let's have a bath!" one of them suggested, rather mysteriously. Bed and three Alka-Seltzers would have had much more appeal for me but I was, after all, in Sweden to try to understand the customs of the country, and this one seemed one of the most surprising. I could not say no.

We taxied out to Gunnar's house in the suburbs, where I discovered that the "bath" was a homemade *sauna* or Finnish-type steam bath built in his back yard.

He had obviously been anticipating some such eventuality, since his wife, after a telephone call, had the little cast-iron stove red hot. It felt like Needles under the midday sun, as we went in, leaving our clothes in an entryway, and our towels gave welcome protection against the sharp heat of the shelves on which we stretched ourselves.

Gunnar poured a dipper of water over the stove, and the tiny room was filled with a cloud of steam that was at once stifling and a relief. My companions relaxed immediately and took up the conversation where it had left off in the café.

"Of course we have the highest living standard in Europe," Pär went on, "and"—a little maliciously I thought—"according to some of your American journalists we have built a modern Utopia here. But we have our problems, too. You have seen some of them, but there are many a visitor overlooks, especially when he is passed on from one bureaucrat to another."

He sharply criticized the Swedish medical profession as being "overspecialized."

"We have some of the best doctors in the world," he said, "but they are not interested in you, only in the disease that is their specialty. If you are old or worn out, or just generally sick, you'll have a hard time to get into a hospital. You often need influence, and there is no influence like that of an obscure disease."

Gunnar rolled off his shelf and poured more water on the heater. When, through the clouds of steam, I expressed surprise that an "advanced" country like Sweden should not have the best hospital accommodations for all, Pär pointed out, "Our housing is bad here, too. People are crowded into little flats, they have no privacy, and it's even hard to get one of those flats. Our cities have been growing so fast that we

just haven't been able to take care of people. Shortage of
flats, hospital rooms—even ambulances. If you have an accident on the edge of Stockholm, it may take an hour for an
ambulance to get to you. We have an old country, but we're
still feeling growing pains, or maybe I should say, again."

I did not tell him of the abominable conditions in some
American hospitals (I did not want to get away from the subject of Sweden) so I relaxed to enjoy the steam and the
warmth. After an hour or so of this, Gunnar jerked open the
door to another room and said, "In you go." The room con-
tained nothing but a tub of cold water into which the cubes
of several ice trays had been dumped. I was being given the
honored guest's privilege of the first dunk.

There was nothing for it so I lowered myself into the icy
water that provided no shock at all. My exterior surfaces were
so thoroughly baked that I should have had to stay some time
in the tub to feel the cold.

After a brisk rubdown—I was spared the birch switches—
I felt as though I had not had a drink for days; and we went
out to another café and more essence of the potato. Perhaps,
I thought, the *sauna* explains how the Finns can absorb so
much alcohol without dissolving. But how can Swedish cities
absorb so many people?

.

Another conversation took place in an Asian country. It
was in the early Point Four days, and perhaps because I was
known to be not entirely enchanted by the Point Four program, the local team of Americans invited me to sit down
with them for a couple of hours of discussion of what they
were doing.

The agricultural specialist, whom I later came to know and
respect greatly, was the only member of the team who was
absent. I was also favorably impressed by all the others, with
one exception. They were highly competent, selfless, sincere
men—and one woman, the chief medical officer. (The ex-

ception was the educationist who, without the slightest understanding of the culture of the country, or even its language, was going to develop a school system, presumably along lines laid down by Columbia University's Teachers' College. I could not help wondering how he would be regarded by the country's intellectuals who include some outstanding savants.)

We talked a couple of hours—mostly I listened—and I could not have had a greater sympathy for Sisyphus. As official government representatives they were presenting an official point of view. They were looking forward to building dams, sinking much needed wells, training men comparable to our county agents, spreading hygiene, teaching teachers. Everything, or nearly everything, they were doing was "good" by itself.

Their dilemma lay in the fact that none of these things they were doing, or planning to do, existed in isolation.

As I thanked them at the end of the discussion, the doctor walked out to my taxi with me. She is a rather famous character in the public-health world, admired and respected by her colleagues.

"Trouble is," she said when we were alone, "the others keep telling me I'm undoing everything they're doing!"

As governmental officials they undoubtedly did not feel free to admit this to me, even off the record. They knew that the country where they were working, already one of the poorest in the world with a daily income for each citizen of less than the cost of a pack of American cigarettes, would double its population in forty years or less, largely as a result of their efforts.

I wondered how a fine group of such obviously idealistic and dedicated people could shut off part of their minds—the part that cares for human beings—and not realize what they were doing to them.

·

Another conversation took place in Japan—and again in a bath. (Hot water is better than wine for making conversation flow, for it brings relaxation without confusion.) We had had a grueling day, visiting the rich gardens that in Japan pass for farms. The thermometer stood in the forties and we were storing up all the heat we could against the cold of the room where, shivering, we would eat dinner while the drafts eddied around us.

We sat in water up to our chins, water so hot that it had seemed almost unbearable when we slipped into it after a cold shower. The drinking order is also reversed in Japan; the *sake* comes after the bath.

I expressed my admiration for the land management I had seen that day, superior even to that of the intelligent and better educated Swedish farmers; and like another world in contrast to the land destruction that is all but universal in the American tropics.

Hideya was pleased by the appreciation of the American visitor. "But," he said, "it's not nearly good enough. Even with the help of our fishermen—and I think they are probably as good as our farmers—we still can provide only about 80 per cent of our food. And as you know, our diet is only barely adequate.

"The agricultural reforms of the American Occupation were a great help. And we think we can still increase production by one-half of 1 per cent a year for a few years, at least. But our population is growing more than 1 per cent a year. We are absolutely dependent on world trade to make up the balance. And trade competition is getting tougher."

Awareness of population pressures is amazingly widespread in Japan. The problem is constantly discussed in the newspapers, which probably reach as high a proportion of the people as in any country in the world. Even peasants I met, with two- or three-acre farms, discussed the population situation in an intelligent and informed manner, and seemed to recognize that they were playing a significant part in the national struggle to survive.

Hideya had a strong subjective reason for concern with the problem; he and his family are part of the tiny Roman Catholic minority in Japan.

We discussed the population problem for days. He is one of the most honest men I have ever known and there was no attempt, in his thinking, to minimize the danger (he pointed out how it had motivated the militarists who brought on the war), and he did not at any time even hint that, somehow, the Lord would provide. He is a scientist, and a Japanese.

He also faced a personal population problem. "When our last child was born we were very glad she was a girl," he told me. "We can give an education to the two boys, but another . . ."

Even in modern Japan, apparently, the girls are not to have equal opportunities with their brothers. "We are very glad, though, that she came. We all love her very much."

There was not the slightest possibility in his mind of resort to abortion, so widely accepted by the Japanese, or even contraception. I did not consider discussing this solution with him, as I might have with some of my Roman Catholic friends in Latin America. His devotion to his faith and its teachings would clearly make compromise impossible. He possessed a strength and sweetness and serenity such as I have rarely encountered except among a few of my Catholic (and Quaker) friends. I did not meet his wife but he was so obviously happy in his marriage and family life that I felt sure they must share their religious experience.

Since I left Japan he has written me of the birth of two more children—a girl and another boy.

On the other side of the world, I was meeting Don Ignacio again after a lapse of nearly twenty years. He had seemed old when I knew him in 1940; and now he seemed hardly older, though not so plump as he had been. He is *guardián*—wildlife protector—on the guano islands off the coast of Peru and one of the most extraordinary individuals I have ever known. I doubt whether he has had as much as three years of schooling; yet his thoughts had substance and point, and his conversation was meatier than one would usually find at a faculty cocktail party.

He had come from the high Andes, and a lifetime of work under the tropical sun had deepened the natural color of his skin until he seemed almost like one of the pre-Columbian Chimu portrait *huacos*. He would probably never look much older.

His career had been subject to exciting ups and downs, liberally laced with *pisco*, the white brandy of his country, and held together by a high humor. It was good to be with him again.

There was the usual handshake and, *Qué tal?*—How goes it?—and the hesitant *abrazo*, which he had never felt quite comfortable sharing with his old *gringo* boss.

He was well, his son and grandchild were well (his grandchild might well be studied by North American pedagogues interested in well-adjusted, happy children), but his wife had died a few months before. His eyes filled with unabashed tears that I could well understand. She had been a beautiful woman and, I sometimes thought, something also of a saint to have borne so cheerfully with his foibles, which must have been less engaging to live with than to watch.

After catching up on the news of mutual friends we turned to a discussion of things in general. He shook his head. Life was now *"muy cara"* and *"sumamente dura"*—dear and hard —in Peru. He could hardly afford to eat meat once a week. (He was more fortunate than most; his job at least made it possible for him to fish.)

Work was hard to come by; neither his son nor his grandson had a job. Taxes were terrible.

His income was probably $350 a year, five or six times that of the Madrasi. I wondered how many he supported on this income, but he was not the kind of man to whom one could put such a question.

As he discussed unemployment he said, simply, *"Hay mucha gente."*—"There are too many people."

His country's politicians were, meanwhile, crying, "We must build up our population!"

What will be in store for Don Ignacio, in the decade or so that may be left to him?

.

These anecdotes, only partially fictionalized (the real individuals involved would not relish publicity) are deeply meaningful for me because they represent personal experiences and involve people for most of whom I have a great deal of affection.

The personal element, however, is mere chance. Each of these men and women is Everyman. For the phenomenon that is having a controlling influence in the lives of each of them —excessively rapid population growth—is, in one way or another, shaping the lives of nearly all the three billion men, women and children alive in the world today.

There are millions upon millions in comparable situations. In fact, since there are more hungry people in the world today than ever before in the history of the human race, hundreds of millions would be more directly concerned than these few friends of mine. From Haiti and Bolivia, to India and Indonesia, and parts of Africa and China, the dearth of the good things of life—not merely enough rice or maize or mealies—is something that is not only widespread, but growing like the decay of leprosy. To travel through vast areas of the world inhabited by the majority of its people is to encounter misery so nearly universal and so harrowing as to be almost intolerable to us overstuffed Americans who shrink from a challenge to our complacency and optimism.

As this chapter is written reports come of Chinese floods that are sweeping away countless thousands of individuals who have the same sensitivities, the same capacity for suffering as our own parents, brothers and sisters, and children. That the floods and the starvation that follows are to a large degree the result of the devastating actions of their forebears is beside the point—except as a lesson to them and to us that people today are framing even greater tragedies for their descendants. The hunger pains, the weakness, the despair, the merciless—even murderous—competition for the necessities of life; the terror of the rising waters, the buffeting and the choking loss of breath as the victims are swept away, are agonizing enough if we try to imagine them today. They are far more devastating to contemplate, tenfold greater, in a tomorrow that may be only a decade or two away.

These are people drowning also in a human flood—a human flood that could, demonstrably, be checked.

In some few cases, especially in the short view, population growth is bringing a better life and adding to human happiness; this may be true in Australia and New Zealand. It is certainly true in the case of the young mother with a new and desired child. Again in the short view. The welfare and happiness of the child must here be especially considered since its parents have created out of two independent and short-lived cells a sentient being as capable of pain, unhappiness, and despair, as of well-being.

But for weal or woe this population change is having more of an effect on more people than has any phenomenon since the human ancestor began to walk upright.

It is changing work patterns nearly everywhere—both as to quantity and quality, and the pleasure, boredom and disgruntlement with which the work is done. While it is creating new opportunities for work, it is often canceling out others much more rapidly.

It is changing both the quantity and quality of people's

food, and even their clothing. Our enjoyment of life is being basically changed by it.

Political man is being transformed locally, nationally and internationally.

The very face of the earth is being ravaged by the rising human flood. If one can believe some of our scientists—difficult as it is not to suspect them of science fictioneering—the same fate may be threatening other planets in our universe.

The standard of living of literally hundreds of millions is being lowered each year; and this deterioration is by no means limited to the underdeveloped countries.

The changes this population growth is bringing about reach into every part of our lives, our workshops, our schools, our pantries, our kitchens, even the secret places where we make love.

It is setting the stage for the final war, or if that is avoided out of sheer terror, for a series of small wars that may eclipse in horror anything the human race has ever known, and may, despite our terror, send the flames licking out until the main stage catches.

It is the greatest revolution in the history of mankind; and mankind has never before responded with such consummate stupidity and apathy to any threat that was so widely recognized.

Not a single government in the world can be said to have a considered population policy, though the Asians, not shackled by the peculiar superstitions of the West, have been on the brink of doing something about it.

Government leaders, both the elected members and the hired hands, throughout much of the world have come to recognize the existence of a human population explosion. Yet they act as though they had no more power of controlling it than of controlling an eclipse.

The international organizations will, almost publicly, wring their hands over what is happening; indeed, over what they themselves are doing. But they go on doing it and making the situation worse. In private conversations many of their officials will admit that they are running scared. Publicly, although they would not hesitate to jump in and try to control an outbreak of cholera or plague—or, indeed, a local famine —they rationalize their position and say they can do nothing "until they are asked."

Like the fabled rabbit before the threatening snake, they are immobilized by fear. Unlike the rabbit, they are as scared by the harmless snake as by the rattler.

Meanwhile, time is running out. Every added year it takes for the ostriches to shake the sand out of their eyes, the misery potential rises higher.

It is not at all certain that we may not have reached the irreversible point of no return. Ghastly famines are a virtual certainty. Perhaps nothing less will shake our leaders out of their timidity and complacency.

The fact that should chill the blood of everyone of us is that a solution of this problem is not, in the most optimistic terms, going to be achieved easily or quickly. The most effective remedies imaginable will require years, or even decades, to make themselves felt. And we have scarcely begun to acquire those remedies.

That the problem could be solved, *given enough time*, is believed by really informed people. That practically none of the world's acknowledged leaders yet feels the danger clearly enough to try to do anything drastic about it, is equally clear.

Yet there are many thousands of responsible citizens in dozens of countries who are deeply concerned. As so often happens, the people are ahead of their leaders.

But we need more interest and more influence from more people. It is, apparently, only we who can put starch into the leaders' backbones.

We cannot afford the luxury of waiting for someone else

to act. If we have any love for this earth and for the creatures that inhabit it, if we are concerned about our children's future, or even our own later years, it is we who must act.

Not next week, nor tomorrow. Tonight! Today!

If we have not passed the point of no return, it is coming closer at a terrifying speed. One resource for which there is no possible substitute is time.

2

Semantic Flypaper

Things are seldom what they seem,
Skim milk masquerades as cream,
was written in a far simpler age, when milk came from animals fed on grass, not on antibiotics; when the pound and the
dollar were understandable measures of the price of a scarce
metal, not of political expediency; when the contemporary
media of communication were used to communicate, not to
obfuscate; and when bread came, by way of the kitchen, from
grains that had not been "improved," rather than from a fac-
tory-laboratory that turns out a product with only the most
distant relationship to the loaves of W. S. Gilbert's day.

As a Swedish nutritionist put it to me recently, "I have to
eat three pieces of cheese and three pats of butter on my
bread every day to get the nutritive value that my grand-

father got only from the bread made out of the grain he grew for his own flour."

Things have, in a certain philosophical sense, seldom been what they seemed to human noses, eyes and ears. Pantheism and pandemonism are not yet entirely dead. But never, in the history of *this* human race at least, has there existed so great a potential for confusion and misunderstanding as envelops the world today. Nearly three billion people, each with a potential for almost infinite combinations of perception, abstraction, association and derivation, through the most highly complex nervous system yet evolved, are subjected to rising tidal waves of communication which are not accompanied by a comparable growth in understanding and ability to evaluate.

What such communication can do to even a fairly sophisticated people was all too clearly demonstrated by Hitler. Today nearly all the masses of the world's people who would once have been to some degree protected by illiteracy, are assailed via radio and TV by millions of words that symbolize phenomena or notions with which the vast majority have had no experience. To back-country Bantu, or to the Ecuadorean descendant of the Incas who may never have seen a wheel, "democracy" and "differential" will be equally meaningful. When one encounters what has come to be known as "the revolution of rising expectations," in the underdeveloped countries (and it is not at all sure some of them can ever be developed) word control seems almost as necessary as birth control. For a country as intrinsically poor as El Salvador— with no minerals to speak of, with much of its topsoil gone and most of the rest on its way to the sea, with its water resources vanishing, and with its forests little more than a memory—to dwell on rising expectations is to trudge through the desert toward a mirage oasis.

One of the major difficulties we all face—especially if we are writers—is the open-endedness of our words. And since a writer cannot explain, and qualify, every word he uses, every time he uses it, it behooves both the writer and the reader to be aware of this defect of our language.

"Government" is not an abstraction—it is people. It is people in the police station, city hall, the dogcatcher's office, the State Legislature, the House and Senate, the post office, the State Department, Tammany Hall, the fire tower, the local post office, the customs shed, the S.E.C., the traffic court, the Supreme Court, etc. Some of the people are highly competent. Most of them are *primarily* (though not solely) concerned with their own comfort and security. Some of them are indispensable. Others are parasites. One thing most of them have in common, as Professor Parkinson has shown, is building up their own jobs and ranks. As population grows, government grows, controls grow—and freedom shrinks. Japan, under democracy, and China, under communism, show the shape of things to come. They share many disadvantages common to heavy overpopulation.

"Government" also means hundreds of other things. In New York it has long operated through such people as "Boss" Tweed, John F. Hylan and Jimmy Walker (with a brief, conscience-stricken interval under La Guardia). With the blessing of the local hierarchy even when Michael James Curley came out of prison, our ancient city of Boston was happy to be identified for decades with him. Corruption for the benefit of the individual has been fairly rare in Washington since the days of Harding, but privilege for the powerful and favored organized minority—the farmers, white supremacists, organized labor, big business, veterans, etc.—has created in the minds of far too many Americans a skepticism of the Congress.

Even more contemptuous of the citizenry as a whole are most Latin American governments. Chile, for example, primarily an agricultural country with 7,250,000 citizens, is still in the position (*fide* the *New York Times*) of having half its cultivable land in the hands of six hundred to seven hundred families. When the Chilean legislature has displeased the powerful landowning bloc, it has quickly and abjectly recanted.

Most other Latin American countries are governed for the benefit of such *latifundista* oligarchies and the Church and the military forces. The colonial status of the populace has been maintained by their own rulers. Much the same situation is said to exist in Asia and Africa. Rumors of governmental corruption rise up like the stench from the Secaucus pigpens.

And it is not only the ignorant and illiterate who are bemused by the symbols (including words) that make possible the operation of our complicated civilization. When two men of such obviously good will, intelligence, education and experience as Leon Keyserling and Raymond Saulnier, with access to such similar data (for which, in general, again read "symbols") can reach such widely differing conclusions, "truth" seems almost as elusive as the mirage oasis.

The writer or speaker who deals with controversial or "loaded" subjects finds his greatest problem lies in what people think he is trying to communicate, or in what they say about it.

When Job said: "My desire is . . . that mine adversary had written a book," he gave one of the earliest adumbrations of the sitting duck.

I have been savagely attacked by the Russians, because I doubted their Gospel according to St. Marx. They did me no harm by damning me, in Soviet propaganda publications, up and down Latin America. In this instance I could echo Cyrano: *Et je me crie avec joie, un ennemi de plus!*

Other attacks (these days one always suspects there may be a Commie in the woodpile) accused me of racism because I urged a sharp reduction in the birth rate of colored peoples —Ibero-Americans, Asians and Africans. These accusers chose to forget my belief that the United States would be better off with less people, a conviction frequently repeated.

There just are enough "white supremacy" Americans so

that people in other parts of the world may be forgiven if they do not understand that the white supremacist is a pathological deviant in the United States.

Racism, in the sense of hatred of one race by another, seems far commoner today among black folk than among white; and in view of the general cultural level of the Negroes, and the way they have been treated during the past hundred years or so, their attitude is entirely understandable.

It may be, as some of my colleagues fear, that the leaders of the "emergent" peoples will deny to their women such medical benefits as have doubled the life expectancy of women in America, where graveyards once commonly held two or three wives to each husband, because such health measures are advocated by white men and Americans or Europeans. But this is hard to credit.

Nehru and Nasser have already made birth control part of governmental policy; Nehru is backing it with tens of millions of rupees in a country where rupees are scarce. Mboya, Nyerere, Nkrumah are outstandingly intelligent men. If they can understand the economic and political complexities with which they must deal, the agricultural and industrial development that must take place to make their countries "viable," they will certainly see the biological, economic —and humanitarian—importance of bringing to their people *all* possible benefits of modern knowledge. At least this is one of the assumptions on which this book was written—and why it was written.

Death, it is assumed, is not only *not* to be feared, but good in itself, at the proper time. Rarely is it good for the young, the healthy, the happy and the useful. It may be very good indeed for the old, the sick, those in pain, and those to whom life is without hope. The suicide who decides, under certain circumstances, to choose his own time and make a dignified exit, deserves our respect rather than our pity or condemnation. Death is, finally, good for all of us, to make room for those recently born or those to be born. The capacity of this earth is finite.

Man is not the only creature whose welfare and survival are worthy of consideration. Other living beings, from protozoa to apes, have some degree of right to their own pursuit of happiness. Any assumption contrariwise must be based on theologically anthropocentric grounds or on the assumption that might makes right. I have never been able to find any other convincing argument as to why I have more "right" to space, food and freedom on this planet, than has—let us say —a canvas-back duck. In the struggle for existence that has produced such fine creatures as the canvas-back and man, through natural selection, some competition and killing for food have been both necessary and, it seems to me, justifiable.

Killing for space may also be necessary. However, some "lower" animals in some manner respond to this need in a way that seems ethically superior to human behavior. Many birds, for example, limit their populations by establishing nesting territories from which other—and competing—birds are excluded. The latecomers and the unfit do not find loving-room (as a correlative to *Lebensraum*) and thus simply do not add to the population; were it not for this control, the world might be awash in robins. Other species lay fewer eggs in periods of food scarcity. Some mammals will produce fewer young when population pressures are high or not propagate at all. Much of the "fighting" among other animals (of course including birds) has as its function bluffing, not killing, and directly or indirectly the limitation of population.

I have yet to hear a sound defense of killing for fun, whether of American Indians or canvas-back.

The earth on which we have evolved, and which through its bounty has made it possible for us to achieve the best we have (along, unfortunately, with some of the worst), is more important than man or any other single creature, since the survival of us all—Krillium and concrete dams to the contrary, notwithstanding—depends on the earth, in its almost infinite complexity. When areas are grossly overcrowded to the point where use of the land means its permanent destruction, it is better to let human beings die than to let the earth die, since more human beings can spring from the restored earth. On the destroyed earth, as in much of North Africa, none can live. The habitat is more important than the species that lives in it—a point that anthropocentric *Homo* finds hard to accept.

There is no particular value in ever-larger numbers of human beings (or any other creature). Below a certain concentration (relative to the habitat and economy on which they depend) human numbers may be undesirably low, for purposes of defense, co-operative labor, etc. This is largely a matter of taste. When one has been brought up in Limehouse or Hell's Kitchen, such an environment has at least the attraction of familiarity. If Freud had happened to be born the son of a Norwegian immigrant, living in a sod hut in Nebraska, the structure of psychoanalysis, and of much contemporary thinking about social problems, would probably be very different. The quality of human beings is far more important than their quantity.

The happiness a man pursues—or a child—should so far as possible be of his own choosing, not that of his neighbors, a commune, a youth board or a presidential commission. Generally speaking, the less compulsively involved the individual is with his fellows, especially in America where conformity triumphs over individualism, the more freedom will he have to seek that happiness. The Japanese strait jacket leaves little freedom of choice. In Norway, choice is nearly as wide as it once was on our frontier, though the low concentration of human numbers is there to some degree offset by communication that has increased quantitatively if not necessarily improved qualitatively. The more people there are, after a certain concentration has been reached, the less freedom there will be to pursue happiness.

"Economic man" is a product of astigmatism, and does not begin to represent the whole man. This arises from one fallacy and results in another. One is inclined to paraphrase Oscar Wilde and say that an economist is a man who knows the price of everything, the value of nothing. (This is, of course, not true of all economists, or even of most economists all the time. But it is true often enough, and of powerful enough people, to wield a strong influence on politics and international affairs.)

Economics deals in prices. It develops a measure or map, called "Gross National Product," that purports to represent the sum total of goods and services, expressed in prices that are measured in currency of changing purchasing power. If a road map were constructed in this way, a mile would one year consist of 5,280 feet, and the next of 6,840 feet.* Among these goods one finds wheat, the protein deterioration of which is not taken into account; meat—perhaps poisoned with penicillin that is also part of the G.N.P.; cranberries and lipsticks—laced with carcinogens that have, themselves, contributed to the G.N.P.; coffins; theater tickets; plutonium bought with funds confiscated through the Internal Revenue Service; the toy missiles on the tails of Cadillacs; jet engines—that by their racket offend a thousand, or a hundred thousand, for every one they are serving; the detergents that are fouling our water supplies; such overpriced, underbuilt shacks as John Keats wrote of in *The Crack in the Picture Window;* the new machines to project advertisements on the night sky —as well as the billboards along our highways; the inflated cotton wool that, in America, is passed off as bread; silver

---

* The G.N.P. is "adjusted" periodically to give prices in "constant" dollars; but many of those who use the concept, especially politicians and newspaper writers, are slow to catch up with the change.

putters; in fact practically any "good" you can think of that people will buy. And in the United States you can apparently sell anything to somebody.

Services undoubtedly include those of bartenders and crooners; Carmine De Sapio and Senator Dirksen; naturopaths and chiropractors; morticians and models, not to mention the labors of those who service them; conductors of Kiddylands and publishers of comic books; quiz show participants and recipients of payola; farmers, presumably including those who receive hundreds of millions of dollars a year for non-farming; teachers who teach and those who are merely the bellwethers of life adjustment; social workers who sponsor relief and the priests who, with their tales of hell-fire, frighten women into having more children than they can possibly care for without relief; other government employees; charwomen, Fuller Brush salesmen, the pilots that guide the jet engines back and forth over millions of homes; salesmen to induce people to buy things they neither want nor need; credit men to induce the customers to buy what they can't afford now and probably won't be able to while they are paying for it; and concocters of tranquillizers and prescribers thereof, to ameliorate some of the shocks resulting from the impacts of other parts of the G.N.P. This includes both fads and dis-services.

When all the money for these goods and services, as well as many others, is added together, and amounts to more this year than it did last, or is greater per capita in this country than in Russia (or vice versa) we are supposed to feel highly gratified (or vice versa). If the goods and services cost less, then our "economy" is shrinking and we are supposed not only to worry but to print more money so that people can buy/do more things they really don't care about, and our economy can expand.

It is very confusing to the layman, and it is comforting that the professional also finds it so. "Economic growth is such a mystifying process," said *The Economist*,* "that no one can really tell from the past what will happen in the future, except that there will be growth of some sort." The last three words give this astute journal a sizable out, and bring one back to the fallacy that the G.N.P. is a measure of value. To some of the uninitiated it seems much more like a measure of the movement and dilution of money.

However that may be, there are so many things of importance to man that cannot be measured in monetary terms —and these include so many of the greatest importance—that "economic man" seems like a figment of a somewhat blurred imagination. (When the G.N.P. becomes a general test of value, much as the Holy Trinity and Our Lady were in the Middle Ages, one wonders whether we are really progressing. At least, in the Middle Ages, there was something to lift up men's hearts.) Clean air to breathe, and clean water to drink (as opposed to water heavily charged with poisons to kill the contaminants), do not show up in the G.N.P. Neither does quiet, one of the most precious and rarest commodities (if it may be called a commodity) that seems to occur in inverse ratio to the G.N.P. As a million people flock into a national park, in automobiles whose average cost is $2,500, having traveled hundreds of millions of man-miles at x cents per mile, the G.N.P. swells like a snake that has just swallowed a gopher. Yet as these millions trample the forest floor, the G.N.P. is in no wise diminished because the bloodroot has been wiped out, the lady's slipper ground into the mud, the water-thrush driven to seek some spot where he cannot hear human beings—or they him.

Has the value of the land and of life not shrunk with these losses? Does a case of Coca Cola compensate for a patch of May apples? Yet these are things I cannot find weighed in any mention I have seen of G.N.P.! As the steel mills go up along

* References follow, page 235.

the Indiana dunes, the G.N.P. will undoubtedly swell—and
our Midwest will lose beauty that only thousands of years
could contrive out of wind, soil, plants, animals and rain. Yet
the loss of the dunes will not be charged against the G.N.P.

The G.N.P. assumption is especially important as we are
using it as a guide to "helping" people in other lands. If, one
reads over and over again, the G.N.P. can be made to rise a
few per cent more than the population, our development
plans will be a success.

One of the major casualties as we pour out billions of dollars to help develop the world in our own image, will be
peace of mind. As we change old ways and force new ones on
folk around the globe—and we do force them, if only by
our use of D.D.T. and penicillin—we destroy old "certainties," ancient feelings of security. But these do not matter because we assume that man is "economic man"—and we are
inflating the G.N.P. In this book this assumption is scruti-
nized with a considerable degree of skepticism.

What we are doing, directly or indirectly, to the beauty
spots and the wild life of two continents, Asia and Africa, is
not only a chapter, but entire books, of which we should be
ashamed. Hundreds, perhaps thousands, of forms of life that
have been brought to exquisite beauty, and are of unplumbed
scientific interest, by the refining interactions of natural selection through thousands or even millions of generations,
are being thoughtlessly or ruthlessly destroyed—and destroyed
beyond possibility of re-creation. But we give them little concern if only we can expand the G.N.P.!

This book assumes that the greatest curtailment of birth
rates must come among the non-white populations. The only
reason the strongest recommendation is made for a cut in the
birth rate of the colored peoples is that they are in greatest
danger from excessive growth. It has nothing to do with
race. Americans, I trust I make clear, would also be better off
if we would reduce our "reproductive enthusiasm" much

further than we have, to the level of our death rate, as the French, Irish, British and Scandinavians did, approximately, in the 1930's. But more about this, elsewhere.

The actual structure of government, as opposed to some political ideal, creates problems that the framers and administrators of our foreign and mutual aid policies have chosen to ignore and which our language helps to confuse. When, for example, foreign aid is provided to the Dominican Republic it is aid not to the people of the country, who hate their government, but to the ruling military and Dictator Trujillo. That we have been supporting him, as we did Batista in Cuba, Perón in Argentina, Somoza in Nicaragua, Benavides in Peru, Franco in Spain and Salazar in Portugal, to name only a few, is well known all over Latin America. (Both our political parties have been involved.) And then, when a revolutionist like Fidel Castro attacks us from the Hemisphere's rostrum, we are as surprised as Norman Douglas' cow that stumbled into a hole and wondered how she got a sore behind.

Yet with whom can our government deal, if not with governments? We have been underwriting corruption overseas, certainly at a cost of hundreds of millions of dollars hard-earned by the American taxpayer, since Chiang Kai-shek was the horse we were backing on the Chinese mainland. According to the press we have continued to do it with "mutual security" funds. With much of this underwriting we are incurring the dislike, if not the outright hatred, of millions of victims of nonrepresentative governments. A government is a government is a government . . .

When our State Department becomes entangled in semantic flypaper both the reader and the writer may be excused if, unless they exercise unusual caution, they find themselves confused. Let no Chilean take umbrage at anything I may say about Chile unless he is sure he is the part of Chile about which I am writing. When I criticize the Roman Catholic Church I am not criticizing all Catholics, many of whom have been among the most admirable people it has been my good fortune to know; I am not criticizing the dedicated parish priest, who literally gives his whole life to his flock; I am not criticizing much of the Church's theology whose beauty and majesty I can appreciate, even without believing it. I am criticizing adherence to doctrine that has little to do with conditions in the twentieth-century world and the tyranny by which the Church (read: Churchmen) attempts to force its beliefs and behavior patterns even on non-Catholics. Above all I criticize the Church's attempts to dominate the mind of man, of whatever faith.

Benjamin Franklin, perhaps the most intelligent American we have yet produced, more that two hundred years ago said: "God helps them that help themselves." This is an assumption, it seems to me, that still possesses considerable validity though as populations grow and become more institutionalized the individual is more and more at a disadvantage in helping himself.

Why should we fly in the face of such godly standards and help those who will not help themselves? One of my Puerto Rican neighbors, an elevator operator and handyman, has five children and lives in a flat nearly twice as large as mine, for which he pays about $12 a room. The balance of the cost of housing him and his irresponsibly produced brood is borne by his neighbors, through "government" funds.

"Government" is here put in quotes to emphasize that "government" does not itself have money to do anything. (It may be objected that "everybody" knows that: I doubt if my Puerto Rican friend does. And certainly many who do "know" it, tend to let it drop from their awareness.) Government, as has been suggested, is many things, but as a disbursing agent it is merely a manifestation of the police force moving money from your pocket and mine, to somebody else's or, to be fair, from somebody else's to ours. It is not the government that subsidizes the elevator operator, the farmer, the veteran, General Franco, the airlines, the U. S. Lines, the trucking lines, etc., but you, the taxpayer, by thousands of dollars you would probably prefer to spend on your children's education, an annuity, a better house and new car, books, bourbon and movie tickets. Would that newspapers would stop printing "government" when they mean taxpayer!

It is assumed that we (our "government") should so far as possible follow Franklin's godly example by helping other people who will help themselves. (When, for our own ends, we are attempting to influence other governments politically —as in the cases where they threaten to succumb, for a price, to Communist perversion—it is assumed that we should at least be honest enough not to fool ourselves by our political salesmanship. We are, after all, the nation that produced David Harum. Political pay-offs are one thing. Genuine attempts to help people are something else again.) Why you and I, who work hundreds of hours a year to support our own bureaucracies, which may or may not be worth what we are paying for them, should work additional hours to support the bureaucracies of other countries, especially when their governments do not begin to tax their citizens as does ours, is difficult to see. Furthermore, there seems to be no more justification for subsidizing the irresponsible breeding of people in other countries, by supplying them with "foreign aid," than for subsidizing irresponsible procreation of our own citizens (as we do) from New York to Los Angeles.

It is assumed, in this book, that the Almighty Dollar is not a cure-all. There is a large and vociferous group, calling itself "liberal," that is convinced the world can be saved and the underdeveloped countries wooed into the democratic pew by 2 per cent, 3 per cent or 4 per cent of the G.N.P. of the West—or at least of the United States. Life, in the countries of Messrs. Mboya, Nkrumah, Nehru, Rhee, Kubichek, Chiang Kai-shek *et al* is not so simple. Education, understanding of government, a favorable physical environment, integrity, skill, the right resources in the right place and a desire for democracy, cannot be bought off the shelf like canned tomatoes.

Latin America has been "democratic" for nearly 150 years, yet only Uruguay and Costa Rica may be said to be "democratic" in our sense. Frondizi and Kubichek govern (as this is written) by courtesy of the armed forces. Mexico made a gesture of freeing itself but its truly indigenous revolution has been largely sold down the river; a group of Mexican women is terrified to have it known that they set up a birth-control clinic lest the Church, which forty years ago supposedly had its fangs drawn, close them down. When half or more of the adults in these countries are unable even to read or write, democracy is a phantasmagoria. And both the proportion and number of illiterates are rising because the people are outbreeding the development of school systems and, above all, of competent teachers. The latter are not made out of whole cloth in five or six years, even with dollars. Lederer and Burdick set forth some of the complexities in the postscript to *The Ugly American*. Others are brilliantly analyzed in Peter Ritner's *The Death of Africa*. The assumption that the problem of the underdeveloped countries can be solved with money is nonsense. Economic man is not big enough.

If democracy is unattainable, what takes its place? Communism? Dictatorship? Oligarchic rule? Did Woodrow Wilson throw open a Pandora's box with his doctrine of self-determination? From Taiwan to Cuba, this question remains unanswered. And the masses of the people, with their "revolution of rising expectations," are scarcely satisfied.

It is assumed throughout this book that Liebig's "law of the minimum" functions in human as well as in physical relationships. No chain is stronger than its weakest link. The International Cooperation Administration builds a twenty-six million dollar fertilizer plant in Korea—and then discovers that the Koreans do not know enough to run it. Hundreds of millions of dollars (though not nearly enough to satisfy them) are sent to the Latin Americans. A sufficiently high proportion of this aid is spent on reducing the death rate so that the population explodes far beyond the capacity of the countries, even with such aid, to expand necessities and amenities fast enough to provide for a population doubling in twenty-three years. This book assumes that such inflation of human misery is a form of cruelty that is unintentional; that we who have made it happen have a responsibility to reduce, and if possible, wipe out, the misery of the millions we have kept alive to suffer.

It is not assumed—it is barely hoped—that we shall be intelligent enough in the future management of foreign aid programs to make sure of at least a tolerable sort of life for any peoples whose continued existence results from our activities. We have no right to prolong their lives into a hell-on-earth of famines, ignorance, tyranny, sickness and hopelessness. What some people think may happen to these men and women and children in some putative future existence is beyond our purview. Our responsibility is to them now, in this life.

And our responsibility is even greater to our own children and grandchildren. When, through our efforts, we help to double the population not only of our own country but of the world in forty years, and that of the world again in perhaps another forty years, we are setting the stage for a kind of pageant that has never before been enacted. Is it going to have the kind of setting the actors will enjoy—that we should enjoy were we members of the cast? The size of the cast, and the kind of setting it acts in, may still be to a large extent within our control. I assume we shall care enough for our descendants in the next two generations to want to make that control beneficent.

None of these assumptions is particularly startling (or profound) though some of them will have been dropped into the dustbin of the forgotten by many people. Some will be challenged.

They do not begin to exhaust the unconscious assumptions on which this book is based. The structure of our language is such that to set forth all the assumptions, conscious and unconscious, behind the book would require more pages than the New York telephone directory.

We live in a complicated physical world in which causes —usually complicated and interrelated—are inevitably followed by effects. Sometimes we can control these. At other times we cannot even foresee them. Often we do not even take them in when they happen.

The impressions our senses abstract from the "real" world of molecules and atoms are always incomplete and, therefore, to a greater or lesser degree misleading. To these impressions we apply words and other symbols, that mean different things to different people, and upon these impressions and symbols we base assumptions that may be expressed or unexpressed, or even unconscious. Communication between individuals, and even more between differing groups and cultures, is complicated—and at times breaks down—through the interactions of such symbols, abstractions and assumptions. A few of the more important assumptions on which this book is built are expressed, but much must inescapably be left unsaid. We are far too prone to forget that one man's hamburger is another man's sacred cow.

3

The Mushroom Crowd

MANY ATTEMPTS HAVE BEEN MADE BY DEMOGRAPHERS
and others to tell us, in terms we could grasp, what is happening to the human population that is swarming over our already
crowded earth. The most vivid statement I have seen came
from P. K. Whelpton, former director of the United Nations
Population Division. He pointed out that if our population
had grown, since the beginning of the Christian era, at the
rate it has during the past hundred years, *for every human
being now on the face of the earth there would be a million
more.* New York City alone would have not eight million people, nor eight billion, but eight trillion—nearly three thousand
times as many as inhabit the whole world today! There
would, of course, not be enough space for them on the surface of the globe, unless they were heaped layers deep.

The world's population is at least for some decades going to go on growing at an even faster rate than now. In terms of absolute numbers and perhaps percentages, this is a statistic that may well be worth more attention and respectful thought than any other measure with which man is concerned, including the rate of atomic fall-out.

There is, of course, nothing new about "population explosions." They have been known, though not labeled with this name, to farmers through the centuries. Some insects, such as locusts, seem to have a built-in dynamic of wild fluctuations in numbers. The plagues of locusts and field mice, which are nothing but population explosions, have been familiar to us in stories as ancient as the sagas and the Old Testament.

The modern professions of animal ecology and wild life management have been largely concerned with animal numbers, and they have described many instances of massive increases of a number of species.[1] Populations of bacteria and viruses have periods of explosive spread and growth; and human beings are in effect overgrazed as are our eastern woods in the presence of too many deer, and sicken and die in large numbers.

Nature has evolved some very effective means—some of which man is already feeling—of controlling population explosions. History shows that these drastic controls will be very uncomfortable indeed. We have little time left to grasp what is happening and to protect ourselves against the tragic consequences of our own blindness.

Though it may have its comic moments, the normal, predictable drama in this play of numbers is always a tragedy —death is the lot of us all. In some species, numbers are kept relatively stable by built-in checks that keep birth rates in line with death rates;[2] in others, numbers normally crest to a peak and then crash like a wave on a beach. The shape of our contemporary human population curve is alarmingly like that of a comber; and the lee shore may be not many decades away.

This type of population curve is not characteristic of mankind. It is self-induced.

Until the very recent past, in terms of human history, the desirability of untrammeled reproduction could rarely have been questioned (except for the toll it exacted of unfortunate mothers). But since our world has so greatly changed, we should do well to take a long look backward to see where and what we have come from.

There is, of course, no history to guide us through most of human time, though there are limited paleontological and archeological remains, and recent, pertinent evidence from our knowledge of such primitive tribes as the bushmen and Australian aborigines.

Man, as a species, is between five thousand and ten thousand centuries old, depending on whose dating you accept, how you define man, and the possibility that there are still, undiscovered, even older human remains. In order to make these calculations easy, I shall assume that man is one million years, or ten thousand centuries, old. If his history were to be written in a book of manageable size, each page would have to cover about fifteen centuries. Only five or six lines would be available to chronicle the entire Christian era, and less than one line to cover that of the entire world since the founding of the United States, and the development of the Industrial Revolution.

Agriculture and town dwelling can go back only some ten thousand years or so, a mere 1 per cent of man's existence or six pages in the book. Until very recently, on this time scale, reproduction began early enough and death came soon enough so there were probably four completed families each century, making up a total of forty thousand human generations.[3]

Since for about 99 per cent of man's existence, he was a relatively unprotected, wandering hunter and fruit gatherer, he remained extremely vulnerable to changes in climate, to droughts, widespread fires, epidemics, large predatory animals and other very effective limiting factors. Local populations must often have been nearly, if not quite, wiped out, as happened in India before the integrative influence of the British made famines extensive rather than intensive. (In pre-European days, when populations were smaller and transport even more limited, crop failures and hunger would be limited to a few hundred, if not a few score villages. Now, the little food there is, is spread over a doubled population; and such monsoon failures as have occurred in the past era may cost millions of lives.) The United States has been shipping to India four hundred thousand tons of grain a month on an "emergency" basis. This will be no more than *hors d'oeuvre* if famine hits one hundred or two hundred million.

It would probably not be far from the facts to estimate that out of every thousand primitive human beings, between forty and sixty died every year, most of them in infancy. The death rate may have been somewhat higher and there would, of course, have been some fluctuations both from year to year and throughout longer cycles. But normal mortality was likely around this figure.

It is obvious that man must have had a birth rate that was equivalent or slightly higher. Had it been lower—and it is almost certain that some strains and local groups of human beings suffered from this disability—our species would obviously have died out.

Primitive life expectancies have been estimated from twenty-one to twenty-five years. "Be fruitful and multiply," was sound biological advice in the ancient world.

The grouping of people into villages, towns and cities resulted in ever greater protection against human and mammalian enemies. The beast of prey was no longer much to be feared (though tigers still take their toll in India) and wars destroyed, proportionately, fewer lives than they formerly had; on the other hand, early crowding into unsanitary towns must have increased the mortality from some epidemic diseases, as it now enormously increases vulnerability to atomic attack and perhaps the effects of stress.

Plagues presumably wiped out entire isolated populations and it is certain that they took a fearful toll that reached its most dramatic and best-known maximum in the Black Death that swept Europe and Asia in the fourteenth century. The effects of this lasted for hundreds of years, so slow was the comeback. It is estimated that one hundred million died of influenza after the First World War but this represented such an insignificant proportion of the increased population—probably four or five times as large—that the consequences of the epidemic were scarcely felt.

Whereas ancient wars and the social disorganization that trailed them like a camp follower were an effective means of checking population growth through the millenia, wars today kill more people than ever before—there is far more meat to feed the appetite of Mars—and yet populations actually increase during war.

Famine was a normal part of man's lot over virtually all the globe inhabited by human beings, as it still is or may soon become again for parts of Asia, Africa and Latin America. The last great European famine was, of course, that of Russia, only three decades ago. Although hundreds of people starved to death in Haiti within the past few months, death by out-and-out starvation has recently been rare.

Because the Four Horsemen of the Apocalypse have been pushed from their saddles, we are prone to assume that they (still excepting war) have been unhorsed forever and that as a consequence a more glorious future lies within our grasp, if only we will reach out for it.

We are, perhaps, assuming too much.

For while we have undoubtedly bettered our condition in some ways, we have done it by control of the environment in which we live. For better or for worse, this control is far from complete, nor are we certain that it will not slip through our fingers.

We have also controlled our internal environments, through changes in our endocrine system, and manipulations of anti-bodies and other aspects of our corporeal physics and chem-istry. What these changes are doing to the seed of new gen-erations and to the various physiological systems of our own, is still far from understood. One thing is certain: the nervous processes that express themselves in understanding, communi-cation, and the relationships among human beings, are often neither comprehended nor governed; and their very unruli-ness may have the direst consequences in our relations with our external environments. The frightened ignoramuses of Little Rock and Birmingham may be an unconquerable ob-struction to an understanding between the world's colored people and the white minority, which is a small minority indeed.

Out of the tangled webs that make our modern world look, at times, like a picture painted by a Jackson Pollock gone mad, certain elements stand out as though the artist had somehow added neon lights. None of these, not even our understanding of the atom, is more striking than the starkly dramatic drop in human death rates.

This is a process that moved slowly, like a snowball on a slope barely steep enough to push it off balance. Then the slope steepened, while the snowball grew in size, and it has now dropped precipitously like Vergil's descent to hell.

There were, of course, no world censuses two thousand years ago—nor, for that matter, are there reliable data for the whole world in this census year of 1960—but population students have indulged in some highly sophisticated specula-tion that has given approximations probably not far from the facts.

At the beginning of the Christian era, after five hundred thousand to one million years of human evolution, it is thought, there were about two hundred million people in the entire world—less than the United States alone will have in 1975!

Sixteen centuries later, about the time of the founding of the new world colony of New Amsterdam, this world population had little more than doubled.

By the time of the American Revolution, world population had grown nearly 75 per cent more; and a hundred years ago, it had added about another 75 per cent.

In the past hundred years it has jumped a startling 150 per cent to almost three billion, or fifteen times what it was in the time of Christ; and if it continues to grow at the current accelerating rate, it will increase more than six-fold in a little over a hundred years.

It has grown like the proverbial mushroom, and as it has exploded in our face, far more deadly than the Amanita, it has taken on the sinister shape of the nuclear blast's mushrooming cloud. Towering up on a nearly straight stem, it has spread a vast and violent head that threatens to crash down and destroy us all. Meanwhile its fall-out has begun to poison the lives of many of us.

The forces and processes behind the formation of this mushroom crowd are far more complex than those that, in the studies of the mathematicians, and in the laboratories of the physicists, evoked the nuclear jinn.

Several of these forces have been so frequently written and talked about, especially during the past dozen years, that little more than a brief reminder is needed here. Four popular and fairly extensive discussions may be found in Fairfield Osborn's *The Limits of the Earth*, Robert C. Cook's *Human Fertility*, Harrison Brown's *The Challenge of Man's Future*, and this writer's *Road to Survival*.

In brief, there have been three major revolutions, two of which are continuing the agricultural revolution which resulted in substantial increases in production per acre and helped to fill the widening gap between what the European had been raising, and what he needed for his growing numbers. Famines were, however, recurrent to the beginning of the last century, even in Europe. But agriculture improved at home, and new lands were being opened up both to receive surplus populations and to provide additional needed food. Britain still depends on overseas sources for nearly half her food, and for virtually all the oil required to run the agricultural and other machinery. In 1957, in concert with France and Israel, she was willing to bring the world to the brink of an atomic war to protect the oil resources dependent, it appeared at that time, on Suez passage. Like other industrialized but overpopulated countries, Albion is far from feeling a sense of security. The large Soviet submarine flotilla, unless there exist means of submarine defense that have not been revealed to the public, could probably starve England out in six months or less.

Hard on the heels of the agricultural revolution came the industrial revolution. It greatly expanded the transportation of food and other raw materials even, eventually, in such countries as India and China, though the latter nation is only beginning to industrialize. There was a burgeoning division of labor, and countries like Britain, Japan and Belgium which had existed at bare subsistence levels, were able to process raw materials into various products that they swapped, directly or indirectly, for food and more raw materials. This worked well as long as the manufacturers held a monopolistic or semi-monopolistic position; but subsequent textile competition all over the world has cut down production in Lancashire and New England, and we are now more or less blackmailing the Japanese to keep their textiles out of a large part of our market. India and Communist China are both aspiring to take over major sectors of world markets with their cheap products; their low prices result chiefly from excessive and hungry populations willing to work for a pittance. When our business men talk about "pricing ourselves out of the world market," they rarely consider this root cause, nor do our labor leaders when they oppose imports from those they call "sweatshop" manufacturers. When, more than ten years ago, it was suggested that Gresham's law applied to labor as well as to money, and that cheap labor thrives at the expense of, and tends to drive out higher-priced labor,[4] certain critics scoffed at the idea. This harsh fact is now being recognized by American steel, automobile and textile manufacturers, though amazingly few seem yet to have recognized the causal relationship between cheap labor and overpopulation. Overpopulation may, of course, fundamentally alter the influence and significance of the industrial revolution.

(Another aspect of the Industrial Revolution has been the development of the internal combustion engine which has made "economically" feasible the destruction of a million acres of good farm land a year, in the United States alone, for the extension of roads, airfields and factory sites. What the damage adds up to, internationally, because of machine-induced erosion, is incalculable; but it is especially severe and widespread in the Tropics, where populations are growing most rapidly.)

We have been buying time to cope at least temporarily with the Paul Bunyan blows of the agricultural and industrial revolution, though it is far from clear we have bought enough.

A third and more explosive change—the so-called vital revolution—has enormously complicated our task.

This began thousands of years ago with the slight drop in death rates resulting from improved living conditions, really headed down the runway after Pasteur and Ross began to understand the basic mechanisms of disease transmission, and took off for the wild blue yonder with the arrival of antibiotics and other "miracle" drugs, as well as new insecticides. Countries that in 1940 had the same death rates as the British Isles three hundred years ago slammed them down to the current British level in ten years. In a number of countries, for example, where malaria, a mere two decades ago was the most effective check on human numbers, the disease has been virtually wiped out.

The gonorrhea that accompanied the uninhibited sexuality of the West Indian, and at the same time sterilized large numbers of women, has in many areas been reduced to inconsequential levels.

TABLE 1[5]

Decrease in Death Rates
1920-24 to 1957

	Per cent
Mauritius	60
Barbados	64
British Honduras	56
Costa Rica	54
El Salvador	40
Jamaica	65
Antigua	67
Chile	57
British Guiana	59
Taiwan	67
Japan	64
Singapore	76

These various factors, interacting in extremely complicated and often unforeseen ways, have combined to send the human death rate plummeting; while over vast areas, usually those least able to cope with the rising tide of people, the birth rate has been but little reduced. In a few populations it has actually increased, so far as available statistics inform us. One of these is the West Indies, as a sequel to the drop in gonorrhea.

Something of the magnitude of the change is shown by Table 1, above. Most of the areas listed are rather small, but this is largely because comparable statistics are not available for India, most of Latin America and Africa. Many of the places listed above, it should be noted, are of immanent importance to Americans.

Rapid growth has been compared by a number of people, including some sober-spoken scientists, to cancer. The late Dr. Alan Gregg, of the Rockefeller Foundation, speaking to the American Association for the Advancement of Science in December 1954, said: "I suggest, as a way of looking at the population problem, that there are some interesting analogies between the growth of the human population of the world and the increase of cells observable in neoplasms [cancer].

"To say that the world has cancer, and that the cancer cell is man, has neither experimental proof nor the validation of predictive accuracy; but I see no reason that instantly forbids such a speculation. If such a concept has any value at the outset, we should quite naturally incline to go further by comparing the other characteristics of new growths with the observable phenomena related to the extraordinary increase now noted in the world's population. An estimated 500 million in A.D. 1500 has grown, in 450 years, to an estimated population of 2 [sic] billion today. And the end is not in sight—especially in the Western Hemisphere.

"What are some of the characteristics of new growths? One of the simplest is that they commonly exert pressure on adjacent structures and, hence, displace them. New growths within closed cavities, like the skull, exert pressures that kill, because any considerable displacement is impossible. Pressure develops, usually destroying first the function and later the substance of the normal cells thus pressed upon. For a comparison with a closed cavity, think of an island sheltering a unique form of animal life that is hunted to extinction by man. The limited space of the island resembles the cranial cavity whose normal contents cannot escape the murderous invader. Border warfare, mass migrations, and those wars that are described as being the result of population pressures resemble the pressures exerted by new growths. We actually borrow not only the word pressure but also the word invasion to describe the way in which new growths by direct extension preempt the space occupied by other cells or types of life. The destruction of forests, the annihilation or near extinction of various animals, and the soil erosion consequent to over-grazing illustrate the cancerlike effect that man—in mounting numbers and heedless arrogance—has had on other forms of life on what we call 'our' planet.

"Metastasis is the word used to describe another phenom-enon of malignant growth in which detached neoplastic cells carried by the lymphatics or the blood vessels lodge at a distance from the primary focus or point of origin and proceed to multiply without direct contact with the tissue or organ from which they came. It is actually difficult to avoid using the word colony in describing this thing physicians call metastasis. Conversely, to what degree can colonization of the Western Hemisphere be thought of as metastasis of the white race?

"Cancerous growths demand food; but, so far as I know, they have never been cured by getting it. Furthermore, al-though their blood supply is commonly so disordered that persistent bleeding from any body orifice suggests that a new growth is its cause, the organism as a whole often experiences a loss of weight and strength and suggests either poisoning or the existence of an inordinate nutritional demand by neoplastic cells—perhaps both. The analogies can be found in our plundered planet—in man's effect on other forms of life. These hardly need elaboration—certainly the ecologists would be prepared to supply examples in plenty of man's inroads upon other forms of life. Our rivers run silt—although we could better think of them as running the telltale blood of cancer.

"At the center of a new growth, and apparently partly as a result of its inadequate circulation, necrosis often sets in— the death and liquidation of the cells that have, as it were, dispensed with order and self-control in their passion to reproduce out of all proportion to their usual number in the organism. How nearly the slums of our great cities resemble the necrosis of tumors raises the whimsical query: Which is the more offensive to decency and beauty, slums or the fetid detritus of a growing tumor?

"One further analogy deserves attention. The individual cells of new growths often show marked variations of size, shape, and chemical behavior. This may be compared with the marked inequalities of health, wealth, and function so conspicuous among the human beings in overpopulated countries. Possibly man's invention of caste and social stratification may be viewed in part as a device to rationalize and control these same distressing discrepancies of health, wealth, and status that increase as the population increases.

"I submit that if some of the more thoughtful cells in, say, a rapidly growing cancer of the stomach could converse with one another, they might, quite possibly, reserve some afternoon to hold what they would call 'a discussion of the population problem.'

"If Copernicus helped astronomy by challenging the geocentric interpretation of the universe, might it not help biology to challenge the anthropocentric interpretation of nature?" [6]

Another scientist of international renown has projected human numbers into the future. Pointing out that population has been growing by 18 per cent a decade, Dr. Harrison Brown of the California Institute of Technology had this to say:

"We have to realize that at some point in time population growth must stop.

"Let us do some simple arithmetic and assess the conse-

quences of continuing population expansion at the present
rate. Let us assume that this growth continues decade after
decade and century after century.

"At this rate, in 730 years [closer to us in time than Magna
Charta] human beings will cover the land areas of the
earth and will be so tightly packed that each of us will be
able to own on the average estates which will be one square
foot in area. Let us assume that by this time, however, science
has come to our rescue and has taught us how to grow food on
the tops of our heads, or perhaps to convert ordinary rock
into tasty, digestible and nourishing delicacies. The growth
will continue and in less than another century human beings
will have covered the waters of the oceans and the population
density of the earth as a whole would then be one person
per square foot.

"By that time we will be eating our way down through the
granite and basalt beneath our feet at a fantastic clip—and
1700 years from now humanity will have achieved the satis-
fying goal of weighing as much as the earth itself. Normally
this milestone in human experience would be cause for great
rejoicing—but difficulties appear. Having eaten the earth there
is nothing left to eat and people grow hungry.

"But science and technology again come to the rescue and
after but a momentary wavering of the birth rate, the population returns to the level of 18 per cent per decade. We learn
to feed upon the planets and then directly upon the sun itself.

"By this time the sun has been replaced in its orbit by a
sphere of thriving human beings and the radius of the
sphere is increasing rather rapidly. Another milestone will
be reached 2,400 years from now, for by then this ball of
humanity will weigh as much as the sun—except for the fact
that by then the sun will not exist at all for it, like the earth,
will have been eaten.

"About 3,300 years from now, the radius of the sphere of
humanity will equal that of the earth's orbit and will increase

at the rate of 55 million miles per year. As century follows century the velocity of the expansion of the sphere will increase.

"Finally, 5,300 years from now, a dreadful day, the insurmountable crisis confronts us. By that time, the sphere of humanity is expanding at the velocity of light, and as we know from Einstein's theory of relativity, it is impossible to travel any faster! From that point on, the rate of population growth must fall—and as the sphere becomes larger and larger, the rate of growth must eventually fall to zero.

"Thus, the theory of relativity provides us with a rigid proof that our present rate of population growth can be maintained for at most 5,300 years, no matter how clever we are— no matter how energetically we pursue science and technology and profit from new discoveries.

"I doubt if even Albert Einstein himself was aware of this hidden implication in his theory!" [7]

This little fantasy of Dr. Brown's is, of course, an attempt to dramatize the exponential growth of the human race. It suffers from two obvious defects. Some of the "cornucopians," whose faith in technological promise is unshakable, will probably retort, "Einstein's theory is only a theory. There is no reason to assume there is any limit to what science can accomplish. Look what it has done in the past!"

The other defect is that the projection extends too far into the future. Many of us have little sense of history, of the past, and we have even less imagination about and concern with tomorrow. (The thousands of American families who have failed to have their children inoculated against polio are evidence of this.) If we are convinced it can't happen to us now, how unlikely are we to grasp emotionally what may befall our way of life in our old age—and especially the kind of existence our grandchildren will have to endure?

For Americans the imaginative grasp is especially remote. Don't we have the highest living standard in the world?

Haven't we, within the past couple of decades, achieved cars with great big fins, brought Jack Paar right into our living rooms night after night? Aren't we living a little longer each year? Although our food, somehow, costs more each year, we have so much of it we can hardly find a place to store it; we cut down the value of our money, earnings, savings, life insurance every year to pay farmers to grow more. What have we to worry about?

Some of the answers will be given in a later chapter but it might be well for us to remind ourselves again that we are not living in isolation on a rich island on this planet.

We make up only about 7 per cent of the world's population, and it is especially above the other 93 per cent that the mushroom crowd towers most threateningly. It is these people —as will be discussed later—who are doubling their numbers not every forty-odd years as we are, but every thirty or even twenty years. And much of this doubling might not take place if it were not for a number of things we Americans do. On top of the problems we are creating at home, we are piling problems around the world. Some of our leaders recognize them but with an almost neurotic compulsiveness they pile more and more burdens on Ossa's top. It may not happen, but it would seem we should at least consider the possibility we may reach the point of no return, from which it will no longer be possible to go back to a safe, happy, and good life.

This point (if it has not already been reached) may well come within the next forty years, during the lifetime of many of the people reading this book. It is almost certain to come within the lifetimes of their children or grandchildren—unless far more honest, vigorous, intelligent and informed measures are taken to fend off disaster than now seem even under consideration. The people of the underdeveloped countries have frequently expressed their conviction that there is no justification for the world's remaining not only half-slave and half-free, but half-poor and half-rich. "The sense of injustice among underdeveloped peoples," said one of their most eloquent spokesmen, "is aggravated by the spendthrift use of resources and raw materials in many developed parts of the world, and the reservation of vast open spaces of the earth for the exclusive use of races that are climatically handicapped for their adequate exploitation, and the ban against Asian migration. . . .

". . . Modern scientific and humane civilization which seeks to build up a unified world community and to develop human resources and potentialities to the full should adopt a scientific population policy marked by the following feature

". . . a policy of equalization of economic opportunities on a global basis with special reference to essential food-stuffs and raw materials and approximation of the present disparate standards of living of the privileged and under-privileged peoples, calling for no further increase of the already high standard of comfort of the privileged peoples who are now in a position to satisfy all their felt wants. . . . It also implies a reorientation of the value and culture pattern of affluent societies in the direction more of non-material services and imponderable values than of material goods and services, leading to new dimensions of human living and adventure." [8] Dr. Mukerjee went on to call for an "abolition of the present dual standard of living in two hemispheres," with a calm assurance that by its very absence of emotion was the more impressive.

Will we, perhaps doubling our own population by the end of the century, accept a cut in the use of the free world's raw materials—we are already using more than one-half—as our requirement doubles? And are we, at the same time, to continue to build up not only the demand, but also the rock-bottom *need* in the underdeveloped countries? The size of the head on the mushroom crowd is largely of our making. And we blow it up more every year.

Do we even have a right to do this? It is being questioned,

and not only in the underdeveloped countries. At the 1954 United Nations Population Conference in Rome, the Reverend Father Stanislas de Lestapis, S.J., generally considered to be the representative of the Vatican, pointed out "the inequality in the distribution of available supplies," and asserted that, "on the present basis of distribution" the United States with, probably, 9.5 per cent of the world's population in 1980 "instead of consuming, as at present, 50 per cent of the raw materials produced in the entire world, would be consuming 83 per cent."

Lord Simon of Wythenshaw, one of the foremost students of these problems in Great Britain, wrote to the London *Times:* "The United States is consuming the world's reserves of fuel and minerals at an almost terrifying rate." Quoting the report on future consumption, drawn up by President Truman's Paley Commission, Lord Simon concluded: "The time will come when the underdeveloped countries will require on a far larger scale than at present fuels and minerals . . . If the U.S. and other Western countries continue depleting world reserves at an ever-increasing rate, the prospects of industrial development by the underdeveloped countries will be black in the extreme . . . is the West ethically justified in consuming world reserves at this rate?

"Ought we not be content with what we are already doing, at least to the extent of slowing down or stopping altogether the increase in our population?" Lord Simon raised the same question in the House of Lords.

The destination to which some pro-natalists would bring us was set forth, somewhat surprisingly, by a Franciscan, Fr. Raymond De Martini, in a doctoral thesis published in 1947 and reprinted in 1955.[9] It carries the "Nihil Obstat" of Francis J. Connell, C.SS.R., S.T.D., and the "Imprimatur" of Michael J. Curley, D.D., Archbishop of Baltimore and Washington.

This thesis—accepted by the theological faculty of the

Catholic University in Washington—maintains that nations in extreme necessity have a right to the superfluous lands belonging to other countries. Dr. De Martini also states that if all peaceful means of obtaining such land fails, a war of conquest is justifiable.

He specifically chooses war over birth control. "If a nation is constantly on the increase in population . . . should not the authorities impose the practice of birth control on the people? Their precaution would automatically preclude the need . . . of conquest. . . . However, birth control is . . . no peaceful means of solving such a problem. It is a violent attack on the natural law, the law of God . . ."

In 1791 Thomas Paine wrote: "Every age and generation must be free to act for itself in all cases as the ages and generations that preceded it. The vanity and presumption of governing beyond the grave is the most ridiculous and insolent of all tyrannies."

We have more or less accepted Paine's dictum politically, but socially, economically and biologically we do it the greatest possible violence. Our population policy, national and international, though it scarcely deserves the name of policy, condemns not only our generation but millions of our descendants to a way of life many of us would find unpalatable or unbearable. It is even possible that the population trends we are establishing, not only by the things we do but also by the things we do *not* do, will drive thousands, and perhaps millions, to mass murder and suicide in years to come. Yet this governmental do-nothing policy has had the explicit endorsement of President Eisenhower, himself.

It is hard for those of us who for years have been aware of population problems not to attribute such thinking—or lack of thinking—to failure in understanding.

This is an especial difficulty of Americans. When one has never known hunger, it is almost like comprehending a new dimension to put one's self in the place of the man who has rarely, if ever, been free from it. I have met scores of Americans who, even after having lived for years amidst direst poverty, simply did not recognize it was there. "El Salvador," said one of them to me, "is such a rich little country!"

It would help the reader to understand this book and hence the magnitude of the problem, if he would try to visualize something of what *every* child that is born is going to need throughout his life. He will need food—one thousand to two thousand pounds a year; water—up to one thousand gallons a *day*, if he lives in a highly industrialized society such as America; land—varying amounts depending on fertility, the skill with which it is used more or less, and the input of labor and capital, but probably averaging an acre; housing— already inadequate, by American standards, for most of the world's people; education—well over half the people in the world cannot even read and write, let alone having a start on education; medical care—there are probably more people who are worse off, from the point of view of medical care, than they are even with regard to literacy, et cetera.

This year, and next year, and the year after that, some one hundred million babies will be born. About one-half as many people (unless there is a war, a pandemic or a major famine) will die. This will leave an added number of *new* people, whose needs must be satisfied more or less in accord with the estimates just given, of about fifty million a year. Fifty *billion* more pounds of food! Fifty *billion* more gallons of water *every day*, if living standards are to be brought up to those of America.

How many are fifty million? How fast are they arriving? It will help to understand if you will find your pulse in your wrist, below your thumb.

Count it for a few seconds.

Assuming that you have a normal pulse beat, it will not quite keep up with the increase in world population. The growth in numbers of empty stomachs. With the rising wave of desperate people. Every time your pulse throbs, the population of the world will have added more than one human being.

For a few nights, after you go to bed, count your pulse. And think what this means, in terms of population growth.

It will help you to understand—though it may not help you to sleep.

4

The Mote and the Beam

June 15, 1975
Minneapolis, Minn.

Director,
French Tourist Office
New York, N. Y.

Dear Sir:

My daughter, who is studying art, will graduate from college in two years, and I should appreciate it if we might have three tickets to see the Mona Lisa on the morning of July 1, 2, or 3, 1977, when she, my wife and my son will be in Paris. If it is not asking too much, they would also like to visit the Eiffel Tower, either No. 1 or No. 2, the following week.

Very truly yours,

John Adams

New York, N. Y.
November 28, 1975

Mr. John Adams
Minneapolis, Minn.

Dear Sir:

Enclosed herewith you will find a card of admission for two, to the Louvre, for 10:45 A.M., July 2, 1977. We regret that we cannot provide cards for your whole family, but bookings are very heavy for that summer. May we urge you, unless you already have hotel reservations within walking distance of the Louvre, to be sure to allow plenty of time to reach the building since tickets are good for only half an hour. Because of overcrowding in the Metro, workers are given preference, and nonworkers must often wait considerable periods for transportation. There may still be time to reserve a taxi through your travel agent. However, on account of congestion taxis are not permitted to wait, and return transportation may prove difficult.

We regret that both Eiffel Towers are sold out for the entire summer.

Very truly yours,

Jean Dubois

Such an exchange of letters may not take place, but it very well could. If you have never heard of Eiffel Tower No. 2, it is because it does not exist. However, R. A. Piddington, pointing out in a recent book that Eiffel Tower No. 1 had reached the point of absolute saturation in 1954, with 14,069 admissions on April 19, suggested the possibility of Eiffel Tower No. 2. The French are good businessmen; it could happen.

It is only fifteen years to 1975. Your youngest child may then be about old enough to enter college. If you are young enough to have school-age children, the chances are you will still be around in 1975 yourself.

There will be many changes in the next fifteen years, here in America, some of which are completely unforeseeable now. We may expect science and technology to improve our lives in many ways. Cancer may have become one of the curable—or preventable—diseases; and polio may have been banished from all the world as it has now been from the lives of Americans who have had the good sense to take the Salk vaccine. Malaria, which now affects more people than any other disease except malnutrition, if malnutrition can be considered a disease, may well be almost wiped out. There will probably be a cheap birth-control pill that, taken by mouth, will induce temporary sterility. Old people may be freed of the crippling and pain of arthritis. Detection of cardiovascular disease may be improved to the point where few of us suffer heart attacks and strokes, and these may be cured when they do occur.

The threat of wholesale devastation in nuclear warfare may also have been banished from the world. What we shall die of, is not clear. Perhaps we'll be like the grandmother of the Gloucester fisherman who told me that the old lady, until ninety-seven, not only chewed tobacco—she swallowed it. "Tobacco killed that old woman. Ef she hadn't've chewed, we'd've had to shoot her."

Cars will have been fantastically improved, and various housekeeping amenities will have been so radically altered that the housewife who can afford them will really find her chores as easy as child's play. Europe will probably be only five hours from New York, Tokyo ten from San Francisco, perhaps less.

The work week may be down to an average of thirty hours, with longer vacations, which will give us plenty of time to use the new jets.

But along with these triumphs of technology will come many complications.

Before 1975 we shall begin to feel the real impact of the baby boom of the Forties and Fifties, not only in France, but also in the United States—and indeed throughout the entire world, excluding Antarctica. By 1975, in this country, we shall probably have, instead of a population of 180,000,000, around 225,000,000. By A.D. 2000 which, it should be remembered, is not so far away as 1914, the American population may have doubled, or nearly so.

This sudden addition of millions of people, which has never before happened in the history of our country, is certain to have an impact on every one of us alive in 1975, that will be more direct, more personal, more acutely felt in day-to-day living than all the improvements of the technicians. It will be influenced by the work of the technicians—and will, in turn, have a good deal to do with what they turn out. Forty-five million more people will change our way of living, from the kitchen to the bathroom.

Adding forty-five million people to our population in the next fifteen years will mean growing by three times the combined 1960 population of Norway, Sweden and Denmark. With double our population in the year 2000, we shall have more than half that of present-day China.

What will our highways look like in 1975? The 65,000,000 motor vehicles registered in 1956, if driving on the same road, would have filled ten lanes bumper to bumper around the earth at the equator. We should have needed eighty-seven lanes bumper to bumper, New York to Los Angeles, merely to park them.[1] There were about ten million highway accidents in 1956, killing almost forty thousand. In 1975 this number of highway deaths, it is estimated by a member of the U. S. Bureau of Public Roads, may well jump to fifty-one thousand, with 110,000,000 vehicles on the roads. It has been calculated they will travel more than one thousand billion vehicle miles—or two million times to the moon and back. This phenomenon seems far more impressive than shooting the moon with a missile!

Unless life is to be one long traffic jam, ways will have to be found of staggering road use—which means a great change from the nine-to-five day, five days a week, plus the construction of thousands of miles more. Some superhighways cost around $3,500,000 per mile—which means a vast increase in taxes. If you spend dollars for roads, you won't have the money to spend for other things.

The environs of our large cities are now littered with thousands of ugly used-car dumps. These graveyards, like many human cemeteries, are beginning to be filled up. When we are producing ten million new cars a year, how shall we dispose of the old? Will the costs of materials—and therefore cars—have risen so it will pay to ship them back to Detroit to be melted down for re-use?

The price of gasoline has been going up steadily for years, chiefly if not solely because of taxes, but it is likely to climb even more rapidly. Oil wells will have to be deeper, and imported oil will have to bear the extra cost of shipping. If we extract oil from shale, the landscape of Colorado and other western states will be littered with vast man-made dumps. See America the beautiful, now!

Atomic power is not likely to provide much relief within the next decade or two, because of high cost and the far-from-solved problem of waste disposal. The former may be reduced as "conventional" fuel costs rise, if engineers are able to bring down the cost of atomic plants. This is, apparently, not likely to come about in a hurry.

The problem of wastes is, perhaps, even more stubborn. The United States, reports the World Health Organization, "in 14 years has accumulated 60,000,000 gallons of radioactive elements stored in more than a hundred indestructible [sic] steel tanks. The cost so far has been $65,000,000. Some of the elements will remain dangerous for decades, others for centuries and in the case of plutonium, for at least 24,000 years." [2] The word, "indestructible," here, seems somewhat sanguine. There has also been extensive large-scale dumping in the soil, rivers and the sea without the public's, at least, being satisfied as to the safety of the procedure.

Superhighways use up some forty acres per mile, usually of good agricultural land. This loss, plus that caused by erosion, plus that needed for airfields, cities, recreation, reservoirs, flood control, and other purposes, will mean a sizable shrinkage in available farm land. To maintain food production (for 25 per cent more people on 7 per cent less land) will require much more intensive agriculture, which will make food rise in price even more rapidly than during the past several years. Dr. Paul B. Sears, of Yale, former President of the American Association for the Advancement of Science and perhaps our leading ecologist, writes: "The late Robert Salter . . . pointed out that the high yields from hybrid corn were definitely being obtained at the expense of soil fertility. In the corn belt, yields of 100 bushels per acre are now about one-third as frequent as they once were. My guess is that farm surpluses will be only a memory within two decades." [3] We may have to cut down on our consumption of meat (it is now little, if any, above what it was in 1908 despite the fact we are now eating a great deal of what then would have been considered offal) and live more on vegetable products as do most of the people of the world. Meat may be rationed by the Government or by price. Most of the Seventy-fivers will think that we old codgers who remember 25¢ steaks are suffering from softening of the brain.

It is interesting to speculate on some of the adjustments we may have to make. For example, American bacon, in contrast to that of Denmark and England, is largely fat and in the cooking loses well over half its food value. (This is a by-product of using the corn surplus.) As we streamline our way of living, and adopt forced economies, shall we also streamline our pigs and make one slice of pork do what required two in 1960? There is much talk of "farming the sea" and eating plankton. Few of the people who advocate this, I am sure, have tasted plankton. I have and found it to resemble finely ground glass tinctured with cod-liver oil. Though it is unlikely to be acceptable to human beings, it may be fed to cattle if the cost of harvesting it does not remain prohibitive. Will beef steak come to have a slightly fishy taste, like a whale steak? Whales may be nearly extinct by 1975.

Farmers depend more and more on irrigation, yet water is already a scarce resource in many parts of the country. Cheap fresh water from the sea will probably not become available in the next fifteen years, or even forty. Agricultural users are likely to find themselves running short, and many towns and cities may well be rationed. It has already happened, on a short-time basis, in many parts of America. For example, Laredo, Texas, was *completely* out of water for two and a half days in July, 1953. Upstairs toilets backed up into downstairs sinks. Air conditioning and refrigerator units dependent on water could not be used. Slowed sewage flow set up veritable gas attacks from manholes.

Water tables were dropping, during a drought, ten feet a year, and ground water was used at a rate thirty to fifty times recharge. In 1951 the drought affected the water supplies of 274 Texas cities. By 1953, seventy-seven cities were rationing water; eight water supplies had failed; twenty-eight had resorted to emergency sources; and forty came within ninety days of complete failure.[4]

By 1975, few Americans will know what natural food tastes like. Today, only one-eighth live on farms and along with a few exurbanites and gardeners, know how good fresh-picked sweet corn and strawberries can be. Roadside stands, at least those in the Northeast, are now buying—and selling—the same drooping, tired vegetables as the city supermarkets; they have often been shipped hundreds of miles. By 1975, there may be only one-fourteenth of our population left on the land. One economist, considered by many to be authori-

tative, puts the estimate as low as two million! The rest of us
will be eating canned, frozen, dried and dried-out victuals, or
foods that have been preserved by radiation or bactericidal
chemicals. To go out to the garden in the morning and eat
a ripe tomato with the dew still on it may be as rare an experience for an American as a quick look at the Mona Lisa.
The appallingly tasteless food served in most American restaurants and many homes today (tasteless compared with
food in Europe, parts of Asia or South America) is surely
tolerated only because we don't know any better. By 1975,
there will be millions more who have never experienced
good food.

Millions of us now drink treated sewage, as the strong odor
of chlorine attests in such cities as Washington, Cleveland and
Chicago; many more will be doing it by 1975. A recent
drought made it unpleasantly clear to Washington (as had
another drought to London) that its river disposal of sewage
had reached about the ultimate limit; Chicago has been dis-
puting water rights with its neighbors for years. Hundreds
of cities and towns will find themselves in comparable situations as their populations grow. Fantastic amounts of tax
money will have to be found for control of pollution, which
in 1959 was estimated to cost $7.5 billion a year.[5] Grinding
up garbage and running it into the sewer, and thus augment-
ing the load on disposal plants may well become a legal of-
fense.

It is not easy to think in terms of millions, or even per cents.
And changes will touch life at so many points. There will be,
presumably, one-third more telephone and power wires to
clutter the landscape. When hurricanes and winter storms hit,
the sheer complexity may make repair of damage much more
than one-third more extensive. The prodigal use of the landscape for such things as golf courses will certainly result in far
more rationing of their use, such as is now common about great
cities. And with the crowding of the links, one might expect

compulsory liability insurance of the kind now required of motorists in many states. Golf space is not likely to grow at the rate of our population and leisure.

As overcrowding grows greater and cities spread, we become vulnerable in a number of ways the Reverend T. R. Malthus could never have conceived. We need not imagine a threat as impersonal as a blizzard or hurricane. A teamsters' or electrical workers' union could paralyze a great city in a few hours.

The more people we have, the more government we must have. Between 1919 and 1956, our population rose 73 per cent but the number of people on the U.S. government payroll went up a whopping 166 per cent or 4.5 per cent a year. This is still below the theoretical level of 5 ¾ per cent postulated by Parkinson's Law, but it does not include city and state employees, and the county courthouse gang. Obviously, however, when government costs jump from around 3.5 billion dollars a year to 65 billion dollars, it's going to take a whale of a lot more people to get rid of that money and to collect it. With roads jammed with cars, skies filled with jets and schools overstuffed with children, personal freedom of action must shrink.

And as the citizen pays more and more, he counts less and less. George Washington presided over about 4,000,000 in comparison with Dwight Eisenhower's 180,000,000. In 1912, when the last states before Alaska were admitted to the Union, each Senator represented 993,000 people, each congressman 219,000. Today, there are 1,800,000 constituents to write each Senator, and 400,000 for each Congressman. By 1975, the numbers will have risen to around 2,225,000 and 517,000.

I have felt for years that my Congressman and Senator didn't pay me much heed, and if you look at it in these terms, you really cannot blame them. I am now entitled to one-half the attention from my Senator as the year I was born; by 1975, it will be down to one-third.

Obviously these men cannot read their mail, let alone answer it, nor can they maintain personal contacts with more than an insignificant percentage of the people they are supposed to represent. They live in an increasingly complicated world without even the time to read, and listen to, experts on problems the best informed Congressmen could not possibly comprehend. This explains, in part, the growth of our bureaucracy to whom representatives delegate authority. Since, however, the proportion of first-rate men who go into government service is small (there are a few of them), one shrinks from thinking of the blunders we may be piling up.

What is the answer? Double the number of Congressmen? One shudders at the thought! Congressmen would not be Congressmen if they did not introduce bills and this would probably mean twice as many. Members of Congress now admit they often vote on measures without understanding them. Is representative government to be sunk by the sheer number of the people represented?

Not only the Louvre will be overcrowded, with rationed attendance. There is already such a traffic jam at the top of the Washington Monument that the Government has been spending $124,000 so up-coming visitors can get off at the top level and walk down a flight to catch the return elevator. This solution is, at best, merely temporary. New York's Metropolitan Museum of Art, on a recent Sunday, had 36,000 visitors with 20,000 not unusual. By 1975, the planners tell us, American urban areas will have doubled in size; there will be not only more people, but more of them crowded around centers of population. If 60,000 visitors tried to "do" the Metropolitan in an afternoon, obviously the periscope wielders would come off best.

There has been a great expansion of art museums in this

country—though of course not of numbers of great master-
pieces to fill them—but for some reason our natural history
museums have not kept pace. So many shrieking school
children crowd at one time into the American Museum of
Natural History in New York, that one gets a good idea of
historic Bedlam. Yet by 1975, the number of children in the
age group to attend natural history museums may have
jumped by as much as twelve million. There is no indication
I know of that we are preparing for any such influx as this.
Indeed, our principal natural history museums have been
deteriorating financially for years, partly because of inflation,
chiefly because high taxes make it impossible for rich people
to support them as they did two or three decades ago. One
director actually asked his staff to go home before dark to
save electricity. Several outstanding art museums have been
developed in this country since the First World War. There
has not been one added in natural history. The limited number
of people who do have money are more interested in human
artifacts than in the works of the Creator.

This is especially unfortunate since our increasingly ur-
banized children have less contact with nature and less opportunity to know at first hand the kind of world in which
we live. For the thrill of having a chipmunk or a chickadee
sit on their hand, they substitute a picture in a national magazine, which is debased currency, indeed!

Along with the penning up of the children goes the obliter-
ation of wildlife habitat. Idlewild Airport (as an example)
was built by destroying one of the most beautiful marshes in
the New York City area. Florida wading birds that conserva-
tionists for years fought and gave their lives to save are now
being inexorably crowded out by real estate developers. It is
good to live in Florida (in some places) but it is ironical that
people must be settled in the State at the expense of its natural
beauty, almost unique in North America. As it is turned into
one vast suburb, it is difficult to understand its attractions

except that it is easier to manage an air conditioner than a
furnace.

The nesting, resting and feeding areas of our waterfowl
are being invaded for other uses—such as farming and oil
production—from the Arctic to Peru. This is certain to have
an adverse effect on the supply of birds, as the demand increases. If the birds are not to be exterminated, shooting will
have to be further curtailed. There are thousands of sportsmen still alive who can remember when there were no bag
limits, and game laws were almost nonexistent—when there
were half as many people in the country.

The use of our national park system has grown from
seventeen million to sixty million since 1946. If our population is to jump nearly a quarter by 1975, but—with a greater
increase in cash and leisure—our travel-miles by around 100
per cent, you can imagine what is going to happen to our
national parks; park attendance for 1975 is forecast for ninety
to one hundred million. The bears will have to learn traffic
signals, and then the bears will have to be killed, unless the
human use of the parks is also rationed. The bears have likewise been growing in numbers, and you can't possibly combine that many people with that many bears, without someone's getting hurt.

Not only will there be more people and more cars. People
will have much more time to use them. Because there will be
more people than jobs—especially when the workers from
the baby boom start coming into the labor market—the
work will be spread and the work week shortened. This will
mean longer week-ends with tens of millions bucking the
traffic in an attempt to get a breath of unpolluted air; or
longer vacations that, combined with the new jet planes, will
carry millions of Americans from the trout rivers of southern
Chile to the new hunting grounds our forty-ninth state will
be ill-equipped to administer—or, more likely, both. The hundred planes a day over the Atlantic may well be tripled and

quadrupled, and Americans will once more find themselves
fighting Europeans—this time for vintage wines and beds on
Lake Constance. (This, incidentally, the most important European lake north of the Alps, and a natural reservoir, is said
to be suffering significantly from pollution.)[6]

In 1955 hunting and fishing were the country's most popular sports: twenty-one million fished, twelve million hunted.
These included one out of every five persons, twelve years of
age or older. By 1975, the forty-odd million who were under
twelve, twenty years before, will be old enough to hunt and
fish, plus some of those born in the intervening years; this may
add another nine million sportsmen. In 1955, hunting and fishing accounted for more than *half a billion* days of recreation.
In 1975, with an increased population working fewer hours
per year, our fish and game resources will be under much
heavier pressure. There will be less available land for game,
and certainly fewer miles of clean streams for the fisherman.
Will this result in shorter seasons, more hand-reared and expensive game and fish and a general downgrading of the
sport? Will people be shooting each other even more frequently than they do now? Something will have to give!

Fish and game in even distant parts of the world, such as
Africa and the Arctic, may suffer even more from sportsman pressure than those closer to "civilization"; the accessible wildlife can be managed if we have the funds and are willing to spend them in an era of rising prices. In Canada,
Alaska and East Africa, on the other hand, government ex-
penditures may have to be spread so thin that there will not
be enough money to patrol hunting areas and to maintain
them at maximum productivity. Furthermore, in much of the
world—notably in Asia, Africa and Latin America—wild
life will be competing for space with exploding human populations who will need land for sheer subsistence. More of the
Creator's works may be expected to vanish from the face of

the earth. The future does not look bright for the sportsman and nature lover!

These descriptions are more or less orthodox reports of the crystal-ball gazers, first class. But one big question remains to be answered: Where are people going to get the money?

This process of an exploding population is not going to be a cheap one. There will be lots of new customers but for at least the first twenty years of their lives, they are going to be living at the expense of somebody else. One of those somebodies is going to be you. For this increase in population, you will pay, and pay, and pay. In 1957 every worker supported 23 per cent more dependents than in 1946. Yet here the term "supported" is misleading; government policy subsidizes large families in so many ways by tax forgiveness, schooling, free meals, free clinic services, etc., that it is now the taxpayer who largely supports the children in most families, after the second child.

It has been traditional to think of people as economic assets for a number of reasons, one being that they were producers. But we have more producers now than we need; around five per cent of them are unemployed, and it is forecast that during this decade jobs will have to be provided for some 13,500,000 *new* workers. We also have many thousands, perhaps several millions, who are, what is called in backward countries, "underemployed." But they are kept on our payrolls anyway, a great many of them as "featherbedders." With the spread of automation, many more jobs are going to disappear. According to the London *Economist*, for example, "Already [1955] it is known that full automation in the automobile industry would mean that 200,000 men could produce more than the million United Automobile Workers now employed." Labor already has plans to spread the work thinner, to have each man work shorter hours in order to avoid unemployment. In other words, with millions of workers coming into the market each year as a result of the baby boom, we may not only have considerable numbers of unemployed directly subsidized by the taxpayer; there will be millions of hidden unemployed, partial featherbedders, paid for by the consumer.

Alaska and Hawaii, will undoubtedly begin to raid the general purse as they come to grips with the costs of their new political situations. In Hawaii the 300,000 Polynesians of Captain Cook's day have been replaced by 580,000 moderns of thoroughly and harmoniously mixed blood, plus some 55,000 in the Armed Forces.

With a natural increase rate that will double the native population within eighteen years[7] some "45 per cent of the population is twenty years of age or less, and will soon be entering the labor market. Since 1955, the increase of population has not been matched by a proportionate increase in the number of jobs. In fact, mechanization on the sugar and pineapple plantations has resulted in reducing job opportunities, at least in agriculture." [8] We may find, especially should a not impossible depression cut the tourist trade in the next ten years, that we are like the old woman who lived in a shoe and who went out and adopted someone else's brood. Prior to the admission of Hawaii, there was a notable lack of discussion of its demographic prospects.

A leading medical statistician estimates that by 1965 *one half* of all the children born in New York City will be in indigent families. Their parents will not pay for the confinement, and these new citizens will become a drain on the public purse, the taxpayer—that is to say, you—from their first minute of life. Many of them will continue to be supported for years, and many of their families will cost the taxpayer hundreds of dollars a month. It is true that they are "customers," but only by the grace of their fellow citizens. The money for their food, housing, medical care, clothing, education, imprisonment, etc., is taken away from other citizens who, of course, then do not have it to spend on their own families or to contribute to more constructive uses.

New York, like a number of American cities, has for years been going into the red, neglecting its capital plant; it owes more than four billion dollars. Its schools, parks, streets, transit and water systems and hospitals have been deteriorating for sheer lack of funds. For example, in one of the big city hospitals, the average stay of women who come in for the birth of a child is *48 hours*—sometimes less; wards are crowded and lined up like cars on an assembly line, unless there are complications. There is simply not enough money to provide either space or doctors, despite ever-rising taxes. On Fifth Avenue buses, twenty-five years ago, everyone was guaranteed a seat. The way passengers are jammed in today would thrill a Norwegian sardine packer.

In 1956 the U. S. Public Health Service estimated that we were 1,124,000 hospital beds short; at current costs merely to catch up would require the expenditure of more than nineteen billion dollars. Recent studies show, according to the Public Health Service, that a level three times the present volume of hospital construction would have to be undertaken on a sustained basis for the next decade, after the necessary stepping-up period, in order to eliminate all present shortages and keep up with obsolescence and new population growth. If only to take care of our growing numbers of ailing aged, we must provide *every year of this decade* for 25 per cent more than are now cared for—and the same increase in the 1970-1980 period.[9]

A much greater problem than buildings is people. To build a hospital is simple if costly, but to man it with the highly trained physicians required by today's medicine cannot be done merely by appropriating dollars. A committee appointed by the Department of Health, Education and Welfare estimates that the funds for medical research alone should be raised from three hundred million dollars a year to one billion dollars within the next *twelve* years, and the number of people engaged in medical research expanded from twenty thousand to forty-seven thousand. With three to seven years of post-graduate study usually required to train a competent re-searcher, we begin to sense the magnitude of the task. The solution will require far more than money. What might be called the pre-researcher will have to be recruited, in competi-tion with the well-heeled teacher of physics and mathematics and the space technologists. And where are the "recruiters" to be found? T. H. Morgan and Aldo Leopold changed the fundamental thinking within their own disciplines, but only a few intellectual leaders of their status are to be found in any generation.

We now have 132 doctors for each 100,000 of the popula-tion. To maintain this ratio to 1970 will necessitate the con-struction of fourteen to twenty new medical schools at a cost of between half a billion and a billion dollars, and then we shall have to find outstanding scientists and faculties to man them. There is plenty of room for improvement in our medi-cal care today. Is it likely to take place under these condi-tions?

In 1953, more than half of all American children were in families having less than $4,000 a year income, and nearly four million in families earning less than $2,000! In 1955, over half the children were in families with three or more. Obviously these poor people did not pay their share of taxes; in the $4,000, three-child family, per capita income taxes were about $16, and in the four-, five- and six-child family, nothing. The average individual Federal income tax in 1955 was $192. For each of these four-child families, other peo-ple were paying over $1,154 in taxes. These people could contribute little to our markets by buying cars, refrigerators, houses or anything beyond bare necessities. The taxes they paid would not cover the cost of their children's education, their share of highways, defense, and many other facets of public service. The burden of their support was shifted to other citizens and thus made no contribution to net prosperity. Indeed, they *reduced* the purchasing power of their fellow citizens and may, thus, have contributed to the recent recession, since this started in the automobile and durable goods industries that are chiefly supported by the more prosperous among us.

According to James Reston, in 1960, one-fifth of all the children in America were living in families with less than $50 a week income for four people.[10]

But we've only seen the beginning. In 1958 there were about forty-four million school children, growing about twice as fast as the general population.[11] At the recent rate of increase, this school enrollment by 1975 will jump to sixty-five million!

The experience of a Long Island, N. Y., community is more or less typical of what hundreds across the country have been facing and will continue to face. As reported in the N. Y. *Times*, in Plainedge District, one two-room school was adequate for the 35 children in the first five grades in 1947. In 1950 a new seven-room school was opened, and enrollment in the first six grades had risen to 269. By 1951, there were 628 children of elementary school age; in 1954 the school population was just under 3,700, with 2,900 in kindergarten and the first six grades, and by 1955, the enrollment jumped to around 5,000. Between 1948 and 1955, the district school board built four new elementary schools, rented classroom space in churches, and still the children were going to school in split sessions.

It would be hard to do more than guess, with the changing value of the dollar and the uncertain economic situation, how much the taxpayer will have to put up in the next fifteen years to meet the expected need; but classroom construction alone might well run in excess of thirty billion dollars. In 1959 we were short about 195,000 teachers. Should our recent wave of prosperity flatten out (it is actually not nearly so high a wave as many people assume) where will the money come from for these additional school seats, teachers, athletic fields, swimming pools, and other amenities we seem to consider necessary to our school systems? Of course there might be a drastic drop in the pressure if the birth rate should fall sharply, since many of the children who will use the pre-college schools in the next fifteen years have not yet been born. There is little indication that this will take place. And even if it did, it would bring no relief to our colleges. Their students have already been born.

The college problem will in many ways be even greater. So many of our good colleges depend on private funds and because taxes are taking an ever larger part of our income, people simply do not have the money to contribute for college support. The situation is not likely to get better; the Truman-Eisenhower administrations built up the largest peacetime deficits in our history, deficits that can be wiped out only by more taxes or by inflation, which is a form of taxation. (Since 1913 the value of each dollar which includes money saved, invested in life insurance, or spent on government bonds has decreased by about two-thirds.)

During 1940-50, while the real income (before taxes) of physicians went up 80 per cent, and that of industrial workers 48 per cent, college faculty incomes went *down* 5 per cent. If we are to swell the number of college teachers, not to mention improving their quality, there must obviously be a substantial rise in salaries. A recent McGraw-Hill editorial pointed out: "Faculty members have, in effect, been subsidizing college education by personal sacrifices. . . . This arrangement is not only a menace to the cultural and educational life of the nation, it is also a menace to our national security at a time when successful national survival may well depend in a peculiar degree on the full development and utilization of our intellectual resources."

Unhappily, more and more of our education is being taken over by huge state institutions, with such large classes that they are not much better than intellectual assembly lines. The old, rich give-and-take between student and teacher in the small class is not only vanishing; it is apparently to be replaced by the 21-inch TV screen. The latter device has defenders, even among educators, but no one has suggested that the tube can answer questions or discuss a moot point. With perhaps sixty million American children under the age of twenty, most of them nonproducers in 1975, the extent of the burden that will fall on the rest of the population beggars the imagination.

Because individuals' taxes are so largely concealed in one way or another, many of us have little idea what they are costing us in time as well as money. For example, in 1913 a man with two dependents and a $5,000 income worked only four hours to earn the Federal income tax he had to pay; in 1955, he worked four hours, plus five weeks! At a $10,000 salary, his working time jumped from twelve and one-half hours to eight weeks and ten hours. This is quite apart from state and local taxes—income, property, school, etc. Our exploding population is going to send them up in the air, too.

Juvenile delinquency, which often quite naturally continues into adult delinquency, has been increasing in this country, and most forecasts as to its future are gloomy ones.

What has rarely been commented on, is its relationship to population growth. Juvenile delinquency is largely, though not entirely, a phenomenon of slums. It is there that birth rates are highest, as is indicated by the forecast that New York, in another five years, will produce half its children in indigent families.

In 1957 the New York City Youth Board did a study of a sample of 150 "multi-problem" families, over half of which were known to at least five to ten social agencies—some to as many as twenty! The average number of children in each

of these families was *four times* that of the number per family
in the city as a whole. Two-thirds of the children in this
group were in families having six or more offspring. More
than half of the families were totally dependent on public
funds. ("Public assistance," as it is euphemistically called,
costs New York $140,000,000 a year, or nearly 7 per cent
of its total budget, which partly explains why it is neglecting
its schools, hospitals and transportation.) Illegitimate children throughout the nation cost the taxpayer nearly one-
quarter of a billion dollars in 1959.[12]

There are two important factors in this relationship between the overlarge family and delinquency; one is economic,
the other psychological, and the two are often interrelated.

Many of these modern families have a population problem
comparable to that of India or Haiti. They simply have too
many children for their available resources. They are often
recent immigrants, perhaps from Latin America, Puerto Rico
or the South, unskilled and in the case of the former, with a
language difficulty. Each family might support one or two
children, although this would probably involve the mother's
working. (Forty dollars a week is a not uncommon wage for
the fathers.) When they have four, five, six or more children, the arrival of each one becomes another economic ca-
lamity. The mother *has* to work. There may or may not be
adequate care for the children at home; many of them are
"latchkey kids," running the streets unsupervised. The mother
is often so tired she cannot give the children the love and
care they need. Frequently the father gets so fed up he
takes the easiest way out and simply disappears. Situations of
this sort are all too typical of delinquent-child families in
cities across the country. Costly attempts are being made to
reclaim the delinquents, but little to prevent the growth of
such a situation as I have described.

As a corollary to these large, depressed and excessively
poor families, many of the children are so unwanted that

their parents even try to give them away. And the unloved children—the unwanted, rejected ones—psychiatrists have emphasized over and over again become the neurotics, even the psychotics, and therefore the delinquents. We must expect juvenile delinquency as long as this vicious circle of poverty and too many children continues to exist. And it will probably grow as long as we ignore its causes.

Many middle-class parents try, with considerable justification, to avoid sending their children to the public schools of New York and other cities. Yet they find that as their personal taxes increase to meet the rising costs described here, there is less and less money available for good education in a decent environment. The vicious circle of the very poor sucks in the rest of us.

Many people, in search of good schooling and decent living for their families, have moved away from the large cities at a cost to the father of two or three extra hours of travel a day. Now New York City, following the lead of other states and cities, is talking about imposing its own income tax to catch those who earn in the city and spend elsewhere. The fugitives from overpopulated New York may soon find themselves paying for schools in two places.

It has been suggested that the automobiles of 1975 will be different from those we have today. For a while, everyone seemed to want them to get bigger. In this sense alone, they were different from the cars in any other country. Their multiplication, and the further crowding of our roads, may force a permanent reduction in size such as began in 1960. If not, another factor undoubtedly will.

Between 1900 and 1950, we doubled our population. Yet if we compare the latter year with the former, we were taking from the earth two and one-half times more bituminous coal, three times more copper, four times more zinc, twenty-six times more natural gas, and thirty times more crude oil! At mid-century we were using about one-half of the entire

world's non-food raw materials. If our population and economy continued to grow at its recent rate, it is estimated
that by 1980 we should use 83 per cent of these raw materials!

American capital has been developing mines—as our own
production peters out—in Canada, Venezuela, Brazil, Africa
and elsewhere. Obviously it costs more to ship iron ore to
Pittsburgh from Minas Geraes than from Minnesota. And
from years of experience in underdeveloped countries, I
should expect many of them to "nationalize"—i.e., confiscate
—foreign properties as did Bolivia, Cuba, Mexico and Iran.

They are going to need more of their natural resources for
their own people (especially as they industrialize) and if we
get the materials at all we must expect to pay ever higher
prices.

At our recent rate of increase, we should double our population in forty years. Many areas of critical importance to
us, such as Taiwan and parts of Latin America, will double
in *twenty* years or little more. Their problems, discussed elsewhere, are inextricably our problems.

There will be little hope that Taiwan, India, El Salvador, etc., can solve their economic problems without slowing their population increase. Yet we are committed, in one
way or another, to participation in their economic progress.

How can we say to them, "You should try to stabilize
your population," when we are letting ours grow by almost
2 per cent a year and are due to double it in forty years?

Can we count on surplus capital to finance the high cost
of our own population increase, as well as financing development for tens of millions of new hungry people all over the
world every year?

Dr. Earle L. Rauber, of the Federal Reserve Bank of At-
lanta, in 1956 pointed out that in the previous decade *per
capita* disposable income—disposable, that is, after taxes—
had risen only one-half of 1 per cent a year in the previous
decade which was, it will be remembered, one of unprece-

dented expansion in the United States. The rate of increase was so low because of inflation, higher taxes, and population growth—the small part of the pie left over had to be shared among some thirty million more people. And in 1960 Stanley Ruttenberg of A.F.L.-C.I.O. complained, "The average yearly rise in real national product in the past six years has been only slightly greater than the 1.8 per cent annual increase in the population, leaving only a tiny margin of additional output for improvements in national defense, public services and living conditions." [13]

We are, obviously, not doing too well ourselves, in terms of compensating for rapid population growth.

Both for our own sakes, and as an inspiration to other countries, a substantial drop in our birth rate would seem to be called for.

Example is as good a precept, today, as it was in the time of Aesop.

TREND IN JUVENILE COURT DELINQUENCY CASES AND CHILD
POPULATION 10-17 YEARS OF AGE, 1940-57

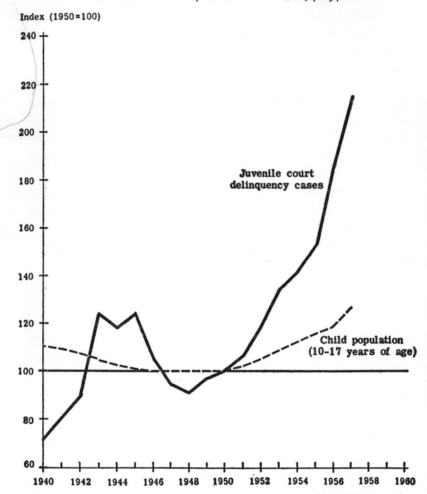

FIGURE 1. Juvenile delinquency has been increasing even faster
than population. While the causes of such delinquency are complicated, much of it derives from excessive population growth.
New York City authorities, looking toward work as a means of
reducing delinquency, complain that there are a hundred appli-
cants for every job "as a result of the baby boom."

5

A Pathology of People

ONE OF THE STRANGE CHARACTERISTICS OF THE HUMAN race is that its members will sit on a tack, grumbling, and not have the gumption to move. This is the situation in which much of the world finds itself today.

According to various United Nations and other authorities, two-thirds, or at the least more than half, of the people in the world are hungry. This means 1.4 to 1.9 thousand million human beings.

In 1750 the *total* population of the world amounted to about 694 million.

In 1850 to 1,091 million.

In 1900 to 1,500 million.[1]

And in 1960, to 3 *billion*.

This the pro-natalists, including many economists, would applaud as progress.

This population growth means that there are more hungry people in the world than ever before. In fact, if we take the higher estimate it means *there are today more hungry people than the total world population of 1900!*

This great sea of starvation and malnutrition exists despite many billions of dollars spent on rehabilitation and development, the so-called surpluses in the United States, and such dramatic and rapid forward leaps in science and technology as the world has never before known. The economists and technicians reiterate their statements and promises of what "can" be done or what "will" be done. Colin Clark, the Roman Catholic economist, even maintains it would be possible to feed twenty-eight billion, or ten times our present population.

What they do not tell us is why there are more than 1.5 billion hungry people in the world *today*.

Their pie exists only in the sky.

The man in the street has little understanding of what is going on, the man in the loincloth, none. They know far too little. The man in the laboratory, paradoxically, is often nearly as ignorant; while he knows so much about a limited area, he may have less understanding of what is happening to people's bodies and minds and to the places they live, than a Mexican peasant. Our highest I.Q.'s stumble blindly under the handicap of channeled vision. Physical scientists, who are as fashionable today as were biologists a decade or two after the publication of *On the Origin of Species*, are spending hundreds of millions of dollars on research that seems totally irrelevant to man's welfare, while hundreds of millions of people starve.

Science for science's sake has become as firmly entrenched as art for art's sake lampooned by Gilbert and Sullivan, while our modern Bunthornes wander with their heads among the galaxies as far as they can possibly get from the caved-in bellies of Haitian peasants.

Periodic reviews of man's ecological pathology are certainly as important as periodic examinations of our consciences. As we live and function in our finite world we are guilty not of seven deadly sins, but seventy times seven.

Few people who read this book will be ignorant of the meaning of pathology: a diseased condition. Many still do not understand ecology: the dynamic and interdependent actions that take place in environments. "For want of a nail the shoe is lost; for want of a shoe the horse is lost; for want of a horse the rider is lost." This book is full of ecological examples.

Physical hunger is only one striking instance of the pathology of people—perhaps not even the most important—and it is the resultant of hundreds, if not thousands, of other interactions. To disentangle them would often be impossible.

Pathology, as it is used here, has so many meanings that to say what it *is* would result in an inadequate definition. At most, I can merely point out a few of the processes it describes.

Pathology leads to a sharp diminution of a "total sense of well-being," which is the excellent description of health adopted by the World Health Organization. It may result in out-and-out starvation with its attendant pain, weakness, desperation, hatred and finally, death. (Such death may come as a benison to the victim—and even to those who survive him who, like shipwrecked mariners on a raft may thus have more to eat. It may also bring sorrow to those who loved him and perhaps desperation to his wife and children.)

Malnutrition, that epidemic tincture of starvation, probably the most universal contributing cause of death in the world today, results in listlessness, depression, lack of energy to enjoy life, including work, love, freedom from pain, the infinite rewards of the senses and the mind. It reduces man not only to less than he might be, but to less than most of the animals about him. What proportion of even the well-fed men and women in the world live at the vital peak of the hummingbird or the leopard?

Malnutrition and starvation make prisons of men's minds

and lead them into all sorts of unsane paths that exist only
within their own nervous systems; vengeful gods and the
search for Nirvana tend to disappear as men are healthy and
well fed.

Hunger shrinks man's greatest function, the power of
thought, and distorts most of the values that justify his considering himself the ultimate achievement, thus far, of the life
force. Cowed by hunger, he seeks the bondage of political,
economic or religious masters. It is no accident that Communist and Fascist agitators find their readiest audiences among
the masses of Kerala, and southern Italy; and that the leaders
of democracy, from Greece to Virginia, have come from the
prosperous classes who were free enough from concern about
creature comforts to accept the not inconsiderable weight of
individual responsibility.

Hunger, often, goes hand in hand with ignorance. The sav-
age who did not know his woodcraft starved. So does the Indian or Haitian who produces six children when he can care
for only two. So would many Americans except that the folkways of their fellow citizens have come to include a strange
compulsion to subsidize irresponsible sexual activity through
so-called welfare programs. (This folkway we are trying to
extend to the rest of the world, but that is another story.)

Ignorance is part of the pathology of our times that, like
hunger, is spreading. There is no question about the fact that
there are vastly more illiterate people in the world today than
ever before in history, and certainly more of what David
Cushman Coyle memorably called "negative literacy." This is
especially characteristic of the student mobs of Latin America, and the millions who, reading their tabloids 365 days a
year, continue in office the political groups, such as Tammany
Hall, that have corrupted American cities. The growth of ignorance is one of the most striking results of the current
growth of population.

Whether lunacy is prevalent in a greater proportion of people today than a century or more ago is impossible to say. (I use lunacy in preference to "mental sickness" since the latter has been stretched to include everything from paranoia and schizophrenia to taking one more drink than one should, or swearing at the boss.) That there are more lunatics in the world than ever before seems certain, if only because there are so many more people. Half of American hospital beds, it is reported, are occupied by mental cases; nearly as many more would seem to be behind the wheels of cars on the highways, killing thirty-eight thousand people a year and injuring a million. That tensions and boredom push people toward or over the edge of lunacy is scarcely debatable.

It would be difficult to establish what proportion of the population is driven mad by, say, the grinding impacts of the human hive. Madness is, of course, very much a matter of what one thinks it is. A ride in the New York subway in the rush hour will turn up thousands of people subjecting themselves to self-torture. Yet Americans, as well as the people of many other countries, continue to form even bigger human clots where contacts, and therefore the potential for friction, rise on an exponential curve.

Life without some human give-and-take would be, for most people, intolerable. The point at which the number of such contacts becomes galling will vary widely with individuals. But that millions are reaching it is clear from the flight to the suburbs (which merely extends, geographically, the contact potential) and the attempted escape to the highways, byways, and the thundering herd of outboard motors that now tatter the peace of all but the most remote waters. The natural habitat of the trillium (where it has not been uprooted or trampled) has become a scattering of beer cans.

Is this exaggeration? Not when you think of the environs of Walden pond, and of much of what was loveliest America. And still less, almost certainly, if we look ahead to the America we shall hand on to our children.

More than a hundred years ago William Cobbett was raging against London as "the great wen." I wish I could imagine what he would say, were he to return today, for he wrote with a diabolic pen.

Cobbett, with a soundly pessimistic turn of mind, was not easily shocked. He rarely expected the best of cities. But even his imagination could scarcely have envisaged the London smog of December 1952 that killed four thousand people and made thousands of others violently sick. "Even the cholera epidemic of 1866 did not equal this," reports UNESCO, "and in the past 100 years only the peak week of influenza in November 1918 produced more deaths over the expected normal than did the smog of 1952. Following the disaster the Government called for an investigation which resulted in a series of recommendations aimed at preventing recurrences. Nevertheless, a similar though less severe smog occurred in 1956 causing an estimated 1,000 additional deaths in Greater London." [2]

Until a very few years ago the great wen remained remarkably self-contained, and within less than an hour from Trafalgar Square, one could find some of the loveliest countryside the world has ever known, virtually unspoiled. But suddenly the wen has become a running sore exacerbated by one of the strangest symbolic devices contrived by our Simian ingenuity, "hire-purchase." The motto of the Englishman, like that of the American, has become, "Never pay today what you can put on the cuff till tomorrow." Installment buying has had such far-reaching consequences in America that we have probably not even begun to understand them. They have operated somewhat like gas turned loose in a very large container. Britain, on the other hand, is a very small container, and the molecules are bombarding each other at a furious and unpredictable rate. Oxford is fighting for its life in the path of the onrushing lorry. The cockneys and their cousins, who still hold on to their slum-dweller customs, scatter the tight little island with ale bottles from Cornwall to Chester. It will be

remarkable if the welfare state does not provide highway facilities to make it possible to strew garbage right up to John o'
Groat's.

According to the *Atlantic Monthly*, "Britain already has
two miles of road to every square mile of territory, most of
them the twisty, leafy lanes that 1.25 million visitors come
especially to see in the summer.

"Yet there have to be new motor roads, for already there is
one vehicle to every thirty-five yards of road. In ten years'
time there could be one to every fifteen yards." [3]

Small wonder *The Economist* comments: "One thing is
certain: if any tangible staple product, from potatoes or blan-
kets to beer or ice cream, had degenerated in quality as cata-
strophically as has the Englishman's weekend leisure, the natural result would have been either a Royal Commission or a
riot. Probably both." [4]

Those modern puritans, the liberals, whose aim seems to be
a leveling-down process to make sure that everyone has as
few privileges as everyone else, would probably exalt the
townies' right to litter the countryside, and even bless the
pollution of air in the name of economic development. What,
after all, does the strangulation of two or three thousand old
folk matter, in comparison with a rise of three points in the
Gross National Product? You can't stand in the way of progress!

Yet in many parts of the world the leveling down is flatten-
ing humanity as though it were being crushed under a vast
hydraulic press. The ecological penalties exacted from the
Haitian people are far more cruel than were the hardships endured under their pre-Republican masters.

There is probably not a part of the world that is not going
to feel the grinding impact of these changes, not eventually,
within the centuries projected by some of the imaginative
science fictioneers, but within the lifetime of most of the people who read this book.

Asia, Africa, Latin America—all three stand in the path of the tidal wave. Europe cannot fail to feel the backwash; France is being undermined now by its Algerian eddy. Something of what is happening to the United States is discussed elsewhere. Only a few of the more sinister aspects of this evolution can be touched on here.

It is tragic and it is frightening that the men and women—especially the women—facing the most desperate situations are those most badly equipped to deal with them. The vast majority are illiterate, with no protection against the lies and blandishments of Communists and national leaders who would exploit their miseries, fears and unreasoning hopes. They are often little more than chattels of their governments, or of financial and landholding oligarchies that function solely in their own self-interest. The greater part of them dwell in countries where climate, poor soils and difficult topography conspire to make advances in even such basic matters as food production difficult. And as long as nothing effective is done about their rapid population growth, their condition is likely to go from misery unto misery.

No region, unless it be Africa, is in a more parlous plight than Asia. Here, according to a recent United Nations estimate, various populations are doubling in about twenty-five to twenty years; and within twenty years may be growing at a rate to double populations again within seventeen or eighteen years! The proportion of children who are, of course, nonproducing dependents and therefore burdens on the parents and the economy, will have jumped to well over 40 per cent within the next twenty years. The resources of CARE and UNICEF are hardly likely to begin to meet the human demands of the next generation, *a generation they have helped to swell*. If hundreds of thousands, and even millions, of children starve it will be in part because of the good intentions of these organizations. They have been conspicuously unwilling to do anything about trying to reduce the birth rate.

According to the United Nations, the ECAFE region (Asia and the Far East, east of Siam) contains more than half the present population of the world and covers only one-sixth of the world's land area.

"In 1956 the population of the region was estimated at approximately 1,462 million, or 53.4 per cent of the world's population; the share of Europe . . . was 15.1 per cent, and the share of North and South America together only 13.7 per cent."

According to this report, the average world density, in 1956 was 515 persons per square mile of arable land; in Europe it was 710; and in the ECAFE region, 975. In southern Korea and Taiwan this density was over 2,600 per square mile, and in Japan 4,636. (These three countries, it should be noted, are of especial concern to Americans.) There is little arable land that can be added to the supply, probably not nearly enough to compensate for what is being lost through erosion.

Yet the United Nations estimates, conservatively, that within a mere forty years the population of this general area may have more than doubled, which of itself would raise the human density of every square mile of arable land to almost two thousand.

If one takes the United Nations' "high" population projection, which is based on an assumption of continuing high human fertility, the number of human beings for each square mile of arable land in the region would jump to nearly twenty-five hundred. Nearly four people would have to be fed from each acre!

Obviously, these people must eat. They do not eat very well now. This undoubtedly has an effect on their life expectancy of about forty-five years compared with our seventy-one. Food production per capita is still less than prewar, when it was far from adequate.

Yet, the United Nations points out, "Very large increases in the food supply of Asian countries are necessary, merely to feed the increasing population at the current deficit standards of consumption. . . . If the current deficit (10 to 20 per cent of available supplies) is added to the increased requirements implied by population growth alone, in these four countries, [India, Ceylon, the Federation of Malaya and the Philippines] the following conclusions emerge: under conditions of unchanged fertility, minimum caloric requirements would increase above present levels of food supply within a range of about 90 to 140 per cent over the period 1955-80; with a considerable decline in fertility of 2 per cent per annum over the period 1960-80 . . . the increase [in food needs] would be reduced by 20 to 30 per cent. Thus, even under the most favorable conditions, it would still be necessary approximately to double present food supplies in the three countries with very high growth rates." (In this calculation, India is the country of "relatively low" growth rate; it is increasing by a mere eight million people a year! More detailed discussion of India is given in the next chapter.)

The U.N. report goes on to point out, in bureaucratic gobbledygook, that in countries where the people live near the subsistence to level a principal result of increasing per capita income is to inflate the demand for food.[5]

This situation was more bluntly stated by a non-United Nations scientist who must, unfortunately, because of his governmental connection, remain unidentified. He writes, in part:

"I find a woeful lack of understanding in Washington of what the fundamentals of the situation in Asia are. Few people realize that overpopulation is at the root of all their economic difficulties and in the case of India it has been almost tragically illustrated in the attempts to implement the second five-year plan. As soon as more money is put into circulation by establishing new industries and giving people jobs, the actual *hun-*

ger is so great that *all of it immediately goes into the purchase of food.*

"There are no savings and no capital accumulation. With an overpopulated area, so close to starvation, any additional accumulations of other people's capital introduced into the economy tends to become consumed immediately so that the normal operations of the capital flow into increased productivity is frustrated. India, consequently, will not be able to implement her second five-year plan, which has to do mainly with industrial development, without a billion dollars worth of food from abroad."

The extent to which the Far East is menaced with disaster is further shown by other U.N. statistics from the same excellent report. While the region, in 1956, had 52 per cent of the world's population, its agricultural production (not all food) amounted to only 32 per cent. Western Europe, with 11 per cent of the population produced 15 per cent of the world's food; and the United States and Canada, with less than 7 per cent of the population, produced more than 18 per cent.

The ECAFE region, it must be recalled, is already the most densely populated part of the earth. It has, relatively, little more land to which to extend its farming. Where it is technically advanced, as in Japan, it has some of the highest production per acre to be found anywhere; there is hope of no more than a little increase. In countries of lesser production, there is such a dearth of knowledge about soils, plant genetics, fertilizers, and such a scarcity of capital and trained men, that even the possibility of substantial food increases is improbable. The greatest technical possibilities imaginable are useless unless they are applied, and the farmers of these countries, excepting Japan, are ignorant, illiterate, superstitious, conservative and often the victims of socio-economic systems designed largely to exploit the farmer. (The usurer and the landlord are frequently all too effective brakes on progress.)

The food prospects are, for Asia, grim indeed.

The future of the Dark Continent may well be even darker. The "medium" forecast for African population growth by the U.N. is from 235,000,000 in 1960 to 517,000,000 four decades hence. With few exceptions, African cultures have since time immemorial been based on low population densities. "So long as there were checks on population," comments *The Economist*, "African farming in general observed the first rule for good husbandry—to keep good cover over the soil.

"But European rule upset the natural balance of this system, since the suppression of slaving and tribal warfare and modern medicine produced a steady rise in African populations. The land available to a larger population was reduced in Kenya, Tanganyika, Nyasaland, French, Portuguese and Belgian areas by the alienation to European use—in most of these it was a small area, but in Kenya perhaps a fifth of the potentially good land, being unoccupied at the time, was taken. In South Africa 90 per cent passed to European use, though much of it in areas not yet seized by the Bantu; in Southern Rhodesia, a country conquered by force of arms, 50 per cent was taken; in Northern Rhodesia, however, less than 4 per cent. Where the Europeans took most land (partly though not wholly as a result), the process of overcrowding shows up in erosion and deterioration most vividly; but even in tropical Africa the effects of a rising population with primitive land techniques can be seen especially in the Ibo areas of Nigeria, in Senegal, and Kikuyuland." [6]

Few events in modern history or, for that matter, in all of history, have been more bestially revolting than the Kikuyu Mau-Mau revolt in Kenya, beginning early in the last decade. There was a sort of insane brilliance in the early organization and leadership of the rebellion in ways that will hardly be lost upon other Africans.

Its root causes lay deep in the needs and the hearts of the people. One of the most skillful propaganda techniques was the publication of books of Mau-Mau "hymns" with words set to familiar church tunes. Over and over again there recurred the cry for space and land. "We are overcrowded in our homes and we no longer have good grazing, good cultivation areas have we no longer, but we are always being called upon to dig soil conservation trenches. . . .

"There is a great wailing in the land of the black people because of land hunger—you fools and wise people alike, is there any among you who is not aware of the overcrowding in our land.

"You Europeans you are nothing but robbers . . ." [7]

Dr. Leakey points out, "Today, in the Kikuyu Land Unit, the population density is such that it is quite impossible for the average peasant to grow enough for his legitimate needs on the land available to him . . . the increase in soil erosion in Kikuyu country was in large measure due to the British advocating methods of cultivation which were not suitable to the light friable soils and steep slopes. . . ." [8]

He goes on to say, "The increase in Kikuyu population over the past fifty years has been phenomenal. This . . . is one of the principal reasons why pressure on the land is now so great. This is not a Kikuyu or Kenya problem, it is one which faces all Africa, India and China to an equal degree.

"No solutions to the other problems dealt with in this book will by themselves suffice, if this problem, which is so closely connected with population increase and pressure on the land, is not boldly tackled. Under no circumstances must birth control be urged upon the African, but when he asks for it we must be in a position to give him something really suitable and satisfactory. And let it be noted that he is already beginning to ask for it. . . . Many Kikuyu, today, openly say they would prefer a small family that they could feed, clothe, house, and educate properly, than a large one that has to exist as paupers." [9]

Along with the growth of human populations has gone a

sharp increase in numbers of native cattle. Control of preda-
tors, tsetse fly and rinderpest, abolition of raiding, and the
economic progress of a part of the population (which often
acquires cattle not for use but as a form of conspicuous
wealth) has speeded up the destruction of millions of acres.
When locust hordes destroy ground cover, it is recognized as
a "bad" thing and vigorous—even international—efforts are
marshalled to fight back. When cattle have the same effect on
vegetation most of those involved will think the herds are a
"good" thing and resist efforts to control them. Millions of
desperately needed African acres are being hurt, perhaps ir-
reparably, by excessive numbers of animals.

Another high roadblock in the path of African progress is
sheer lack of knowledge of the environment. The most egre-
gious example of this was the British groundnut—peanut
growing—scheme of the last Labor government, which produced little more than a $100,000,000 loss. This was followed
by a poultry-raising fiasco, this time under the misguidance
of an American, that cost more millions. Most Americans
(including some who pontificate on the Tropics) know little of tropical agriculture. Yet, few people anywhere know
more than the British. Their failure with the groundnuts is
of extraordinary significance.

The future of Africa floats on a stormy and uncharted sea
of ignorance. Most of the economic progress that has taken
place has resulted from the extraction of minerals by processes that are little dependent on climatic factors. The human
factors involved are changing rapidly, which raises another red
light on the path to Africa's future.

Nationalism and racism together—a quite understandable
distrust and hatred of the white man—are probably an irresist-
ible force in sub-Sahara Africa. The feelings behind the drive
for freedom are peculiarly understandable to Americans who
threw off their own colonial yoke not so many years ago. But
because we understand and sympathize with the African peo-

ple (this by no means excludes a respect for some of the things the French, British and Belgians have accomplished), it is regrettable that the freedom movement is taking place in such an unfavorable environment. There are two limiting factors that may slow or even halt progress, much as a defective carburetor or broken oil pump would slow down, stop or even seriously damage a car. The first of these is the cultural stage in which the revolution is taking place.

That colonial powers have any responsibility toward their subjects is a very recent notion. I can remember nothing from American history of British attempts to raise American living standards through education, economic development, or in any other way. Our ancestors were here to be exploited which is why (like the modern African) they revolted.

Although the little that the British did in India was very good indeed and they left behind them a superb, if minute, elite of technicians and administrators, their failure to do more for the mass of people and for the country as a whole, in terms of education, improved living standards and technological progress seems incomprehensible. The Colombo plan came two hundred years too late.

We Americans, it should be pointed out, are in no position to be self-righteous about the treatment of our dependents. There are few groups of human beings, anywhere, that have been as neglected and abused as has the American Indian. We cannot even shrug off the shame on our ancestors since there has been little, if any, improvement during the administrations of Eisenhower, Truman, or that great humanitarian, Franklin D. Roosevelt. The conscience of the Congress is tormented by what is happening in India, but not by what is happening to our Indians. Life expectancies among our Indian population today are substantially below those of other Americans in the United States.

In the sub-Sahara, the colonial powers have done so little to raise the living standards of the Africans that millions of them are hardly beyond the stone age. Based on division of labor, the large body of specialists on which modern society depends, is almost nonexistent. Well-trained African physicians and sanitarians are rare. So, also, are engineers, agronomists, sociologists, demographers, educators, botanists, geographers, foresters, veterinarians—such experts as will be desperately needed not only to improve the lot of the masses in Africa but to keep them from wrecking the continent altogether. A substantial proportion, perhaps a majority, of the Africans who have had a higher education seem to belong to those two classes of symbol manipulators, economists and lawyers. These, too, Africa probably needs but at this stage of her development she could make far more use of people who are trained to work with the earth and its resources. She is marching into a stormy future with an army that is far more bedraggled and bobtailed than the troops at Valley Forge, and facing far more desperate battles.

The greatest of these, and one that must inevitably shape the future of nearly every other event in Africa, is the explosive population growth already mentioned.

We may perhaps imagine the travail that lies ahead for Africa, with half a billion people in the next four decades, if we compare her resources with ours. She has no food-growing area comparable to our Midwest, or even our irrigated areas and spreading pastures. Illiteracy rates in many areas run above 90 per cent, compared with our 1 or 2 per cent. Africa does not even have teachers.

"Above all," *The Economist* points out, "sustained growth requires educated rural workers . . . Investment since the war on education and other social services has been heavy. But a limit was soon reached, when schools were built for which there were no teachers, university departments with places nearly equal to the number of pupils taking school certificates. The French found that they were placing a recurrent load on budgets equivalent to over 20 per cent of the original capital cost of the services." [10]

In testimony before a U. S. Senate Subcommittee on Foreign Aid in 1957, I pointed out that we were having difficulties coping with our rising tide of pupils, although our annual population increase had been running only about 11 per cent of the number of children in our primary schools.

In contrast, population increases in some of the African countries was at least as high as Morocco's 42 per cent, and almost certain to increase during the next decade or so.

Educationally, Africa is running a losing race with population. As UNESCO pointed out with reference to Egypt: "Although during the period 1900-47 the rate of illiteracy was reduced from 92.8 per cent to 80.1 per cent the number of illiterates 15 years old and over steadily *increased* from about 6 million in 1907 to about 9 million in 1947." [11]

As these young people are uneducated, they are negligible assets of society; and unable to make sense of the world about them, they are more and more likely to be used as weapons by the Communists. In the new Moscow University they will undoubtedly not be educated, but conditioned in the most literal Pavlovian sense.

Our governments—federal, state, county and local—are among the less corrupt in the world though our standards for the behavior of government employees are probably inferior to those of Britain and Scandinavia. In the new African states, corruption is reputedly widespread.

We are finding the expansion of our highway system a considerable burden; Africa has hardly begun to develop hers.

Like India, Africa is characterized by a bewildering lack of cohesiveness. Ghana, for example, "is still less a homogeneous nation than a collection of tribal, or native, states—at least 100 of them—each with its own paramount or head chief, and varying in population from 2,000 to about 250,000. . . . It is

true that many of the country's leaders now think of themselves as Ghanaians, but most of the people still think of
themselves as Fantis, Ashantis, Dagomba, Gonjas, and so
on . . . most of these groups speak a language or dialect of
their own, the only one they would be willing to see adopted
as the official language of the country." [12]

It is in settings of this sort that the New Africa must struggle for breath. The thickheadedness of the dominant South
Africans, the fanaticism of the Algerian *colons*, the grim dog-
gedness of the "white highland" settler in Kenya—these all
whip up the devil's brew that is Africa of the mid-twentieth
century. To provide for nearly three hundred million *more*
people here inside forty years under optimum conditions
would appall Hercules or even that confirmed customer's man,
Mr. Kiplinger. It is impossible to envisage what lies ahead,
given the kind of land Africa is and the state of mind of the
people who live there. It is small wonder that the Communist
fishermen are readying their gear for the troubled waters.

In New Delhi, in 1952, I spent a long and illuminating evening with an Indian physician. What he had to say about India
was unusually intelligent and informed. (More than one Indian has stressed to me their intellectuals' ignorance of the life
in the villages where three-quarters of their population live.)
What was more impressive was this physician's understanding
of Latin America, which far surpassed that of many U.S.
government officials I have met who have been concerned
professionally with the countries south of the Rio Grande;
besides, he had a greater comprehension than some Americans
who have lived in Latin America for years. Those *gringos*,
isolated by their own home-cooked thinking and their lack of
contact with the masses of the people, are to all intents and
purposes still in Detroit or Washington. For the Indian there
were no such barriers. As a public health man in El Salvador
he got out to the places people live. And what he found there
was a world he understood.

"I have never felt so much at home outside Asia," he told
me, "as in El Salvador. If it were not for the difference in language and religion, I might have been in parts of India."

He had undoubtedly come on the country that, in miniature, most resembled his own. While its per capita income is
above that of India it is probably the second lowest in Latin
America, and living costs are far higher than in the Asian
country. Diets are not dissimilar except that maize and beans
are substituted for rice and dal. In housing and clothing, differences are not marked. The two landscapes have the same
raddled look of abused land. Both are almost without fuel
supplies, though the smaller central American country is not
yet reduced to burning cow dung. This is fortunate since
there are few cows.

If my Indian host had gone to Haiti he would undoubtedly
have been as shocked as I when I first visited India and saw
even Salvadorean poverty compounded. People were dying
of starvation in Haiti in 1959,[13] at a rate that would have been
considered a substantial famine had it taken place in India.

Haiti's 3,500,000 people are crowded into a largely mountainous area where the tropical climate is hard on people and
land and where the term "arable land" has been stretched by
the pressure of population beyond all reason. The peasants,
highly illiterate, have for decades been neglected by the
"elite" of the capital. The population is growing more slowly
than it might, in part because of wise and courageous decisions
on the part of health authorities: to some degree, at least,
health programs have been concentrated on extirpating crippling diseases such as yaws instead of recklessly pulling down
the death rate, with the birth rate riding high.

The test of any environment is its capacity to cope with adverse conditions: a chain is no stronger than its weakest link,
and Haiti has many weak links. Undependable rainfall is only
one of them. According to the *Times* more than 45,000 persons were suffering from a thirteen-month drought in a north

coast area that was formerly a productive agricultural region. "Two hundred deaths have been attributed to starvation and diseases arising from malnutrition. Less than a mile into the hills . . . many families are subsisting on green mangoes. This fruit is the only food available to them.

"Hunger is not normal in this area. . . . The arid south coast of this peninsula continually faces famine. But until the drought struck, this north coast mountain area produced fine crops. . . .

"With drought, a depression brought about by a small coffee crop and low coffee prices, and no public works as a result of the country's desperate economic straits, there is little employment. Most able-bodied men have left the region to search for work elsewhere. . . .

"But many remain . . . resigned to their fate and convinced their situation is hopeless. Even if rain comes soon few have seed left to plant or animals to barter for seed. Nor can they hope to mortgage even part of their future crop to seed merchants, since all their assets have been pledged.

"The dead are being buried during the night without services." [14] This statement makes especially poignant the lot of these people, who are nominally Roman Catholics. As one considers their agony versus the great wealth of their Church, one wonders how this can be allowed to happen. The relief, distributed by the Church, according to the *Times*, is in the form of "emergency aid" from the United States government.

The mysterious ways of ecclesiastics may here be matched by those of politicians. Haiti is a close Caribbean neighbor, a fellow member of the Organization of American States and part of an area we consider of prime importance to the defense of our nation. Since the last world war we have spent well over fifty billion dollars on foreign aid. We have, in the words of President Truman, promised "triumphant action against hunger, misery and despair."

Yet only last year, in that tiny country of 3,500,000 people, on our very doorstep, we let people starve to death. It would be interesting to have the answer from Mr. Truman, Senator Fulbright as Chairman of the Foreign Relations Committee, and Dr. José Mora, Secretary General of the Organization of American States, to the question, "Why?"

Haiti's distress is undoubtedly the most acute in the Western Hemisphere, but it is certainly not unique; and it is probably most significant as a projection of what many more millions may be expected to endure as their populations explode more rapidly than in any other large section of the world, even Asia.

There have been recent reports of starvation in Bolivia, and only three months before the news of the Haiti drought came out, the *Times*[15] reported similar situations from the country that likes to consider itself the "greatest" in South America— Brazil. Mobs "demonstrated against hunger, inflation and charges of government corruption." Thousands of people were reported to be without food, and riots broke out from the coast to Manáos far up the Amazon.

Brazil has an area larger than that of the United States (excluding Alaska) with only about one-third the population. Yet this is growing so rapidly that it will double, at the current rate, in less than thirty years, with attendant demands on the resources, discipline, technology, finances, and plain human behavior.

Brazil may well be envied for its space—for the elbow room available to its citizens—but not for much of what fills this space. A substantial proportion consists of swamp and semi-desert. Some of its best agricultural land, especially in the State of São Paulo, has been badly hurt by erosion.

Despite substantially increased efforts on behalf of education, it is fast losing the race with illiteracy. UNESCO reports: "While the rate of illiteracy in Brazil . . . steadily decreased from 65.3 per cent in 1900 to 50.6 per cent in 1950, the total number of adult illiterates *increased* almost two and a

half times, from 6.3 million in 1900 to 15.3 million in 1950." [16]
Population growth is outrunning educational expansion.

And as this book is written, Brazil's financial condition is
frighteningly shaky. It is a country in which almost anything
might happen, even if the United States were willing to go to
exorbitant lengths to bail it out.

More than one Brazilian has said to me, "We have no population problem. We need more people." And while it is true
that Brazil could improve certain economic conditions with
more people, advantageously distributed, it simply cannot absorb so many more people so fast. It is like the drought-
stricken farmer who prayed for rain and got ten years' normal
rainfall in twenty-four hours.

Latin America as a whole is growing at an even faster rate
than Brazil. Only three countries are increasing as slowly as
"developed" areas: Haiti, where people are already starving;
Bolivia, where there is probably some starvation and certainly
much malnutrition; and Uruguay, where, it is reliably reported, there is an extremely high rate of illegal abortions.

Each Latin American country is different from the others,
each has specialized problems and each must confront its rapidly growing demands in its own special way. In general,
however, it may be said that this area, growing faster than
any other part of the world, contains few countries where,
until death rates rise again, the living standards of the mass
of the people may not be expected to fall as a result of excessive population growth.

The entire Caribbean island area is of especial concern to
the United States, and it promises to become, as the Virgin
Islands were once called, "the poorhouse of America." It includes some of the world's most rapidly proliferating populations, and most of the islands are beggar poor in resources.

At a New York Planned Parenthood meeting in 1957, Sir
Grantley Adams, then Premier of Barbados, said: "Barbados
now has a population density of 1,400 per square mile—just

about 28 times greater than that of the United States. Even more startling is the expectation that by 1970, a brief 13 years from now, a further population growth of 43 per cent will occur. This would mean we will have a virtually impossible population density of 2,000 people per square mile, unless natural increase is curbed quickly."

Barbados, with almost no illiteracy, has the highest educational level in the Caribbean; there is a zeal for learning that is unmatched, so far as I have observed, in any underdeveloped country.

Yet education is, in a sense, self-defeating. Barbados has tried to relieve its population pressures by emigration, in part subsidized, only to lose some of its "best and most skilled workmen who leave to find employment in Great Britain." (Puerto Rico has had a similar experience with the United States.)

"Though communism is not a problem in Barbados," Sir Grantley added, "I agree that population pressures in many areas breed totalitarianism and war. We are all aware how the political unrest which often comes from too many people and too few jobs may lead to catastrophe. But I also believe in the democratic spirit. If we can feed the people, give them jobs, hope and self-determination, grievances will disappear. To this end family planning is essential for the future and dignity of man."

Somebody is almost certain to come up with the suggestion that the birth rate be reduced by raising the protein content of the diet. Nonsense often dies hard and this theory, like the proverbial snake's tail, has wiggled through many sundowns.

Based on the century-old folk medicine superstitions of an American poet and dramatist, it was revived in 1952 by a political appointee to the Executive Council (not the technical staff) of the U.N.'s Food and Agriculture Organization.[17] The Doubleday-de Castro thesis is that "nature" compensates for undernourishment by a higher birth rate and that, therefore, overpopulation is the result of, not the cause of, malnutrition.

In support of his thesis, Dr. de Castro presented a table of countries ranging from Formosa to Sweden in which, as the daily consumption of animal proteins ("complete proteins") rose, the birth rate fell. *Post hoc, ergo propter hoc!* Or the baby always comes in the little black bag.

The author does not give the source of his data which makes it impossible to check them.* But there is one curious omission: Argentina.

Now, anyone who has visited the Argentine or who has read much about that fascinating country knows that its citizens (even since Gen. Perón virtually wrecked Argentina's economy) are among the world's most carnivorous people. The United States, pre-Perón, ate almost as much animal protein per capita and now eats more. Yet of the eleven countries listed by Dr. de Castro[18] (who went away back to the Thirties for some of his birth rates) only five had higher birth rates than the Argentine, in 1938, and only one (India) had a higher birth rate than the United States, in 1957-58!

In the table below the countries are arranged in Dr. de Castro's order with Argentina added. The daily consumption of animal proteins, in grams, is taken from a report of Dr. de Castro's own Food and Agriculture Organization, the birth rates (in parentheses) from the U.N. Demographic Yearbook.

If Argentina, with the second highest animal protein consumption and the sixth highest birth rate, in 1943-38, had not been omitted from the table the Doubleday-de Castro theory would, of course, have been knocked into a cocked hat. It is unfortunate that Lord Boyd-Orr, former Director General of F.A. O., who wrote a glowing foreword for the book, did not notice the hiatus. The 1957/58 figures, with the U.S. leading

* For this reason three countries listed by de Castro have had to be omitted since data could not be found.

in animal protein consumption and trailing only India in birth rate, and Argentina tied for fourth place in protein consumption with a higher birth rate than eight of the other countries, should show the error of his ways even to Congressman Glenn Cunningham of Nebraska who, as recently as February 16, 1960, cited the de Castro figures in the *Congressional Record* in an apparent attempt to question the seriousness of the "population explosion."

TABLE 2

Daily Consumption of Animal Proteins, in Grams and Birth Rates (in parentheses)

	1938	1934-1938	1957/58	1957
India	(33.3)	8	5[*]	(39.9 in 1951)
Japan	(27.1)	7	14[*]	(17.2)
Yugoslavia	(26.7)	22	—	(23.7)
Greece	(26.1)	23	23	(19.3)
Italy	(23.8)	20	24	(18.2)
Germany (West)	(19.7)	43	46	(17.0)
Ireland	(19.4)	47	53	(21.2)
Denmark	(18.1)	57	60	(16.7)
Australia	(17.5)	67	59[*]	(22.9)
United States	(17.6)	50	66	(25.0)
Sweden	(14.9)	59	57	(14.6)
Argentina	(22.9)	62	57	(23.3)

[*] 1956/57

For years it has been standard practice in American Planned Parenthood infertility clinics, where attempts were being made to help subfecund couples have children, to check their diet and make sure it included sufficient protein. A number of studies by a variety of investigators have established the unquestionable relationship between malnutrition and *low* fertil-

TABLE 3[19]

Country	Soap Consumption Lbs. per Capita
Australia	27.5
New Zealand	27.5
United States	27.0
United Kingdom	25.3
Belgium	19.5
Canada	19.5
Argentina	17.8
France	16.8
Portugal	11.5
Italy	9.7
Venezuela	9.2
Colombia	6.8
Mexico	6.1
Thailand	1.5
Philippines	1.1
India	0.5
Indonesia	0.2

Various measures, such as the amount of energy used or per capita income, infant mortality rates, life expectancies, etc., have been used in attempts to measure comparative living standards. None of them has been very successful. For example, the distribution of the benefits derived from nonhuman energy may raise the living standard of a small fraction of the population. Even food, although no one can eat much over 3,000 or 3,500 calories a day, may vary so widely in quality as to be a largely meaningless indicator. For example, there is probably little doubt that the Communist leaders in China enjoy far more protein and vitamins than do the peasants. When one measures the distribution of soap, since no individual is likely to want to use more than a modest amount per day, it provides an interesting scale by which to measure living standards. Even here, however, one should enter a *caveat:* That in Venezuela there are such wide differences in wealth and the per capita amount of soap used is so small that, lacking information on median amounts of soap used, we may safely assume that the majority of the people in the country go dirty.*

* Data referred to consumption in 1950 and include total use of factory-produced soap and synthetic detergents (bulk included).

ity. Indeed, investigators in India have forecast a possible rise in that country's birth rate as nutrition improves[20]—if it does.

Some of those, including highly placed people, who have used the de Castro theories as a means of bolstering their "optimism" and theology, or as an excuse for doing nothing, may discount the work of these researchers. It would, however, be hard to convince many people that the Argentines and the North Americans are such deviant members of the human race that their reproductive physiology runs counter to that of the other 2.7 plus billion human beings in the world!

Other areas, all distinctly different, should be considered either because of their importance to Americans or because of their peculiar interest.

The Middle East is the first. This is a political, economic and cultural hodgepodge, about as stable as a dynamite cap, and with a flash point little above zero. The area is of great importance because of its oil which pushed Britain, France and Israel into brinkmanship that must have stopped the late John Foster Dulles in his tracks; because its generally unreliable and undemocratic governments are the kind of chestnuts the Kremlin likes to keep in a low fire; and because its rapidly growing masses are about as superstitious, ignorant, emotional and easily misled as any people on earth. (Israel, growing at a rate which will double in eighteen years, has its own problems, is obviously not typical of the other countries of the "Fertile Crescent"; besides, it can draw heavily on its American friends, with the blessing of the Internal Revenue Service.) A measure of what Middle Eastern leaders think of their people is given by the foolish stridency of Radio Cairo. The United Arab Republic, Lebanon, and Jordan have a natural increase rate of 2.8 per cent a year, which would double their populations, not to mention compounding their problems, in twenty-five years. (Statistics are not available for Iran and Iraq.)

The most desperately beleaguered is Egypt (if the Middle

East may be stretched to include this African nation). As Leigh White pointed out, "In 1798, when Napoleon's invading army awakened the Egyptians from their somnolence, 2,500,000 people were living precariously off the produce of 3,000,000 sparsely cultivated acres along the banks of the Nile. Today [1953], after 154 years of Western influence, and seventy years of total or partial British occupation, 21,000,000 people are living precariously off the produce of 6,000,000 intensively cultivated acres. In other words, twice as much land must now feed eight times as many people." [21] As one flies into Cairo from the east, the desert strait jacket in which the Egyptian people are squeezed is dramatically obvious. By 1960, the population had reached about 26,000,000, and if it continues to grow at the present rate will double long before the end of the century. Food produced on the irrigated acres that may be expected to be added to Egypt by the Aswan Dam, will be just about consumed by the increased population expected during its construction. And the greatest technical skill cannot be expected to augment production per acre indefinitely, if only because of increased costs.

Egypt has more (though not enough) educated and technologically trained men and women than most of the area. One of her most profitable exports, for example, is teachers, and, with effective aid, she can certainly increase her food supplies. But there seems to be little hope that she can catch up with her population growth if it continues; stable government and an educated citizenry may well be even more difficult to achieve. None of it can be realized without massive outside help, and this Egypt is not getting.

The most conspicuous lack in outside help is birth control. Egypt is one of the very few countries in the world to face up to the problems growing out of her high birth rate. She has been extending a chain of clinics that, according to reliable reports, have been well received by the Egyptian people despite the fact the clinics must depend on less than satisfactory contraceptive methods. However, Egypt's foreign exchange position has been extremely weak, and funds have not been available to buy supplies. The International Planned Parenthood Federation has scratched together such money as it could and sent the Egyptians jellies and foam tablets. The United States International Cooperation Administration has, up to early 1960, done exactly—nothing.

Their defense against this criticism I should expect to be that of the American doctor who, now operating a hospital in the Caribbean, offers no help with child spacing because he is "not asked for it!" Whether or not the Egyptian government has requested aid with contraception could probably not be determined by any means short of a Congressional investigation; it is reported on good authority that other governments sponsoring such a program have been tipped off that it would be better not to ask for birth control aid since they would not want to be turned down.

The "not having been asked" excuse is, of course, a contemptible and dishonest attempt at justification for doing nothing in an area where someone might criticize. It is impossible to imagine a physician who would withhold treatment for trachoma or cholera because he had not been asked. And anyone who has had anything to do with international affairs, at the working level, knows that requests for all kinds of projects are constantly, albeit unofficially, "stimulated." Meanwhile millions of diseased Egyptians are being kept alive, as White puts it, in conditions inferior to those endured by any "barnyard animal except the donkey, the sheep and the goat."

Note should be taken, here, of one of the most pitiful groups of people in this entire Near Eastern area, the Arab refugees. "There are," according to The Economist, "more than 900,000 people, of whom half are children under 15

years of age, wasting their lives upon world charity; and
there are 200,000 more, 'strictly speaking not refugees' but
who need relief . . . for whom funds 'are just not in sight.'
At any particular moment there are about 47,000 pregnant
women in the camps. . . . United Nations relief work grows
more efficient with each passing year but the problem gets
worse instead of better." [22]

On these facts, any comment would seem to be superfluous.

Scattered around the world are hundreds of inhabited islands, some of them large like Madagascar, others tiny like the
hundreds scattered over the South Seas. Many of them are inhabited by people and some by such engaging creatures as sea
turtles and albatrosses. Unhappily, many of these islands are
being turned into slums by their human inhabitants, something that does not happen under the condominium of the
other animals. One of the chief causes is excessive population
growth.

Madagascar, Ceylon, Samoa, Fiji, New Guinea, Papua,
Mauritius, the Seychelles, Taiwan, Hawaii, Puerto Rico, Barbados—all are growing at a vertiginous rate. Some of them,
like Puerto Rico, and Samoa, become economic problems—for
somebody else. "We don't have a population problem," more
than one Puerto Rican has said to me, "you have it." And so
we do, in New York, Philadelphia, and more and more mainland areas into which Puerto Rico's surplus population moves.
(It has been pointed out that if the United States had the population density of Puerto Rico it would contain the equivalent
of the population of the entire world; and if we were as
densely populated as Barbados we should have more than
twice as many people as now live on the entire globe!) [23]

Hawaii, doubling in less than thirty years, poor in resources, already dependent on the unproductive tourist
trade, may well become another economic Mississippi within
a generation, especially if we have a substantial depression.

(It is far from certain, it seems to me, that this particular type of devil has been permanently exorcised.) Samoa is likely to become a permanent parasite, if it has not already reached this status.

A number of these areas can also become political migraines; Madagascar is already leading the way. Whatever impact they may have on mainland peoples, their own populations are, in many cases, facing desperate overcrowding, ever lower living standards (shades of *Typee*!) and probable starvation. And while it may be difficult for us to feel much concern about the Malagasy, what happens on their island, in their bodies and minds and emotions, is important to them.

Malta, growing very slowly, has already passed the saturation point. With a population of 320,000, it has water enough for only 250,000; the rest must be imported in tankers. It raises enough to feed the population only about three weeks out of the year.[24] Guided, or misguided, by a particularly nasty lot of politicians, it has a high nuisance potential in the Mediterranean.

The shape of things here and to come in island (and many mainland) populations was neatly summarized in mid-1959. "The prospect of supporting twice its present population within 25 years is a serious one for Fiji. Already the pressure of population on the land is intense in certain areas, and extremely poor marginal land is being opened up for settlement by cane farmers in western Viti Levu and northwestern Vanua Levu. Erosion consequent on repeated burning, overstocking, and overcropping is severe throughout the dry zone and has led to falling cane yields on marginal land; on first-class land the silting up of drains and the deposition of infertile silt by floods has had the same effect. In the dry zone even the second- and third-class land that might be opened for settlement is limited in area, and in Viti Levu the presence of native reserves, water catchments, and areas closed for conservation use makes extension of agricultural land almost impossible.

"It is in the dry zone that the population problem is most acute, and it is the Indian component that is most affected. [Forty-nine per cent are Indians, 43 per cent Fijians.] Existing cane farms may not even be able to continue to support the present population and certainly cannot support the increase; it is unlikely that sufficient new employment opportunities will be available in the towns. For the Fijian population the situation is not so serious, since large areas of native land in the wet zone are still untouched. But even here the land in forest is by no means first class: the most fertile and accessible areas are already in use . . . as the areas reserved for Fijians are likely to be the better areas of native land, it is clear that no remedy will be found through the opening up of large tracts of forest land for Indian settlement. The magnitude of the whole problem is illustrated by the fact that within the next ten years some 7,000 males (of all component groups) may be expected to retire from active employment, yet in the same period nearly 50,000 persons will be entering the work force." [25]

To cope in more than a token way—to cope really effectively—with the Fijian situation during the next two and a half decades is likely to be beyond the resources of the British whose responsibility the Islands are; they have, after all, many other problems and commitments. Small commons almost certainly lie ahead for the Fijians, and for island dwellers in many other parts of the world unless they have sufficient strategic value to use as blackmail.

An island population with a highly developed economy is Japan. Its attempts, twenty years ago, to break out of its island barriers led to one of the costliest wars in history in terms of men and money. Japanese admit freely today that it was largely the rapidly growing population that sparked this misadventure under the leadership of militarists.

In 1939, Japanese population was about 72,000,000; today, a full war later, it is about 93,000,000. This is more than half the total population of the United States, and the total land area into which they are crammed is smaller than the state of California. Only 14 per cent is arable and with as concentrated agriculture as is to be found anywhere on earth, the Japanese produce only 80 per cent of their rather Spartan diet. At one time, after the war, the nation was increasing by about two million a year.

No people, anywhere, probably, is as conscious of its own population problem as the Japanese. Newspapers and magazines discuss it frankly and honestly. In several hundred miles of travel about Honshu, talking with all sorts and conditions of men, I encountered no one who expected to solve the country's population problem by the sort of wishful thinking one finds in many parts of the world—economic development or emigration. In ten years the Japanese, by the free and deliberate choice of individuals, cut their birth rate in half.

Nothing like this has ever been recorded, I believe, in human history. If the International Cooperation Administration were, like the Lord, to help those who help themselves, no one would better qualify for assistance than the Japanese.

There are demographic, economic and statistical papers, reports and books about Japan's population problem but nowhere have I seen a discussion of the all-pervasive influence of overpopulation comparable to that in a witty and informative little "popular" book by Ichiro Kawasaki, a Japanese diplomat.[26] Here we have, quite incidentally, an account of what happens to people, even intelligent, able, hard-working and disciplined people, when they are crowded into too little space. Mr. Kawasaki is singularly free of the handicap of either-or thinking. He does not discount Japanese abilities, accomplishments, or shortcomings; he sees them in relation to one another and as influenced by one another. He tells things that do not show up in statistics.

For example, between 1938 and 1957 when Japan was beginning to ride a boom (largely U.S. financed), the number of unemployed rose some 60 per cent; and there are now in the neighborhood of one million people a year coming into the labor market.

Kawasaki gives us some background, especially in a chapter called "WPA for 88 Million People."

"Throughout Japan, in big factories or small shops, offices or banks, there are great surpluses of employees," he reports. "A maddening ritual takes place whenever one transacts even the most trivial business. One needs only to keep an account with a Japanese bank to get a forcible illustration of this. Painfully often I have watched the way the bank's unoiled machinery works in Japan. I have watched the same procedures in New York, London, Geneva, and many other cities of the world. On some occasions in Japan it has taken as long as thirty minutes after a check and bank book were presented at the teller's window before the cash was actually received. Elsewhere, cashing a check in a bank takes something like thirty seconds.

"Precautions in Japanese banks are sometimes carried to the point of absurdity. What is done is that the teller stamps the check with his seal and passes it back to a bookkeeper, who checks the passbook with the ledger to see that the entries tally. A second bookkeeper enters the new check on both books and passes both of them to the chief cashier, who examines all the entries to see that they are correct and then endorses an order for the payment of the money. A fifth clerk records the endorsement and makes the final check. The documents then go to a sixth man, who, if there has been no hitch in the proceedings and you are still waiting, pays the money. Thus six men who take care of the cashing of one check would not be able to take care of one-sixth of the number of payments handled by Western banks. . . .

"Likewise, most governmental offices are extremely over-staffed and efficiency suffers as a result. I know a departmental chief in the Tokyo Metropolitan Office who, being of high rank, occupies a large room which he shares with one clerk and two tea-serving girls. One of the latter would surely be thrown out of a job in the event that an American electric water dispenser were installed. As for the other, I can see little earthly reason for her presence, except perhaps to answer occasional telephone calls. Whenever I call on this friend, I see these two girls either leisurely sipping tea or languidly reading the office newspaper. . . .

"The great newspaper *Asahi*, an influential eight-page daily, has more than 6,000 people on its payroll. Japanese newspapers, especially those of the *Asahi* standard, have wonderfully edited columns with full coverage of world news, something demanded by millions of subscribers. Yet there is no earthly need for so many employees. What a heyday a good personnel efficiency expert would have in showing how much increased productivity per person could mean in savings to these papers! . . .

"Even in a small office, small employees, except section and department heads, are seated in rows, like soldiers in a mess hall. Although each is given his own work space, desks are all pushed together in double rows so that one person is seated next to another and also facing another. This jamming is a result of lack of space due to overstaffing of the office. This seating arrangement is conducive to gossiping and chatting, which as a matter of fact many employees indulge in. To make matters worse visitors are always shown into the office, even on personal business. Endless hours are spent chatting with friends and fellow workers. No one can avoid hearing the conversations, and everyone is distracted. It is well-nigh impossible to concentrate on one's work under such circumstances. . . .

"Although office workers seem to idle away their time do-ing almost nothing, they have to be careful lest they lose their jobs. In other words, they have to make themselves useful in one way or another, and this often takes the form of insinuat-ing themselves into the good graces of their superiors. For this reason few government officials or office employees ever take prolonged vacations. By law they are entitled to three weeks' holiday during each year. However, very few avail themselves of this opportunity, because they are apprehensive lest while on vacation their places be filled by people who might try to learn the work so well that by the time they return they might lose their jobs because their usefulness had been severely questioned.

"Similarly, officials, especially those of lesser rank, try to keep all important files to themselves and seldom allow others to have access to them. This tactic is obvious. When one man has to remain away from the office because of illness, for ex-ample, he locks up his files. The result is that when his supe-rior wants to find out about a certain matter related to his work, no one else can give a satisfactory answer. The supe-rior naturally misses the absent one, and his importance is enhanced. This artful bureaucratic behavior is conscientiously employed. I realize that the Japanese are not the only ones familiar with this ruse, for I have heard some of my foreign friends decry similar tendencies among their own people.

"All of these petty practices—and some are even evil—are brought about by a surplus of employees, but no organization can drastically streamline its staff, for fear of giving rise to social unrest. . . . Even profit-conscious business establish-ments maintain staffs substantially larger than are actually re-quired. Through the use of labor-saving office equipment, perhaps one-fourth of the present number of personnel would suffice quite well. . . .

"Since everyone has to be employed in some way or another in order to make a living, employees have to quit their jobs at around the age of 45 years or at the most 50. The government employee, for example, usually reaches the top of the hierarchy at about 40 years and then is forced to resign in order to 'make room for those who come in his footsteps.' . . . After retirement, he has to seek some odd job elsewhere. He may become an adviser to some group or institution, usually in a capacity related to his previous position. This is usually a sinecure, but he receives barely enough pay to sustain himself for the several years that he has yet to live.

"The struggle for existence is so severe that the Japanese will often stoop to running down other people, even the closest of friends. Although such an accusation may be completely fabricated, the method can be justified in the eyes of the Japanese. The Military Government Team in the various prefectures during the Occupation used to receive numerous anonymous tips about all sorts of people. They were written with the sinister intent of having the person mentioned get into trouble with the Occupation Authorities. Petty personal gossip involving mutual friends is a part of daily conversation and with many a favorite topic. . . .

"Perennial overpopulation has not only made life miserable for millions, but also has given rise to many undesirable characteristics which have become virtually national. . . ."

Mr. Kawasaki constantly refers to overcrowding in streets, homes, cities and the countryside. In Japan it is practically impossible ever to be alone. The average annual consumption of meat per person in Japan, he reports, is only three pounds, and farmers—including the relatively wealthy ones—subsist almost entirely on a vegetarian diet throughout the year. "Even tender green maple leaves are dipped in dough and fried in deep fat." Americans, on the average, eat nearly twenty-five times as much meat as the Japanese. Kawasaki points out that "ten years of war and occupation brought tremendous changes in Japan's internal situation. Today most of the old sweatshop labor conditions are gone, and workers are strongly unionized. Wages have risen, and working hours are strictly enforced in factories. Of course, owing to the differences in standard of living, great disparities exist among the wage scales of British, American, and Japanese laborers, and these are reflected in the cost of production. It seems to me that such variation in cost is inevitable. As the British worker in many industries is willing to work for less than his American counterpart, so is the Japanese worker willing to work for less than the British. As I look at this issue, it is the question of supply and demand of manpower that is most basic." [27]

Mr. Kawasaki traces the strong authoritarian rule of the Japanese people through centuries and explains that it was in part the reason for the success of the Occupation. "Since orders from superiors are inevitable, once the orders are issued there is no alternative but to obey them. . . . In this respect Japan bears a close resemblance to Germany where 'Verboten' signs are ubiquitous. . . .

"When people are always told to do this or do that, individual initiative is largely suppressed. It should also be mentioned that Japanese lack of initiative is partly due to the extreme congestion of the country. If in a crowded place everyone had his own way, people would be constantly bumping into each other. In a crowded subway all one has to do is to stand still and wait patiently until the train reaches the next stop. There is no room for independent action on the part of individual passengers to relieve the congestion. You are deprived of free movement and thereby lose freedom of independent thinking. . . . [Even when Japanese riot, they tend to do it in snake-dances!]

"I once built a California-style house with a spacious garden around it. Unlike most Japanese houses it had no fence

or wooden walls. . . . A swarm of neighborhood children
would peek through the windows and spy on us while we
were eating or doing other things. In no time at all the entire neighborhood was well informed as to our standard of
living. . . ."

The shape of things to come, as the world's tide of population rises, is projected in a harsh light by this Japanese diplomat:

"In overpopulated Japan, privacy is very hard to maintain. Everyone is subject to prying eyes all about him and is
constantly exposed to the criticism of others. If anyone be-
haves a little bit differently from others, he is the object of
considerable criticism. . . .

"The Japanese cannot mind their own business, largely because they live so compactly that their interests are closely
interwoven. If, for example, an individual occupies more
than the normal space for a house, the other 88 million people
would have that much less room. So they cannot be disinter-
ested [sic] in what others are doing. They would kick up a
row and criticize the individual in an attempt to dissuade him
from occupying such a spacious lot.

"In such an extremely congested country as Japan there
will always have to be a certain amount of regimentation in
order that the general welfare of all the people can be assured.
The general public tends to act and think en masse, since
there are so many individuals that consideration cannot possibly be given to individual desires or requirements. As a result
of this social regimentation, the Japanese have learned to live
together in their crowded islands with relatively few outward
signs of friction. However, ambition is thwarted in the process and the Japanese tend to be petty in many things they
do." [28]

At another point Kawasaki says: "Japan has always to
contend with the problem of overpopulation. Already sixteen million people have to be fed with imported food. Japan

has eleven million more people today than at the time of the surrender in 1945. Moreover, the natural population increase per year is 1,500,000. The economic drag of an impoverished mass plus the additional burden created by a rapidly expanding population cannot be made light of. In these days of mass production and increased mechanization, surplus manpower tends to become more and more of a liability." [29]

"Communism in Asia," says Mr. Kawasaki, "is not like Communism in Europe. The doctrine and goal may be the same, but the reasons people are attracted to it are almost entirely different. In Europe, Communism is an answer to frustrations which are more often spiritual than physical. It is an interpretation of history which provides a satisfactory alternative for those who no longer accept the will of God.

"In Asia, Communism is by and large the direct result of poverty. The most fervent Communists are not necessarily the poor themselves, but those who are disgusted by the corruption and injustice which poverty produces. The masses are generally docile and fatalistic and readily respond to leadership. In Asia, the permanent basis for revolution is that it is steadily getting poorer. The consequent loss of all hope for a better future makes men ready to take desperate action.

"Discontent is spreading in Indo-China, Malaya, Indonesia and Burma because of extreme poverty. It is not alone that wider and wider classes of the population are awakening to the misery of their lives; unless there is economic equality also, poor countries will remain corrupt countries, always offering fertile ground for Communism.

"Post-war Japan fulfills both of these conditions; and the spiritual frustration, coupled with widespread poverty, presents a dangerous situation." [30]

More than 150 years ago, Thomas Robert Malthus commented that of all the people he had visited the Norwegians were the only ones not concerned with enlarging their population; and he theorized that perhaps the resemblance of Norway to an island made it possible for the Norwegians to visualize the possible limitations of their lands.

The population phenomena Mr. Kawasaki considers (his concern with overpopulation makes up only a small part of an amusing and illuminating description and discussion of Japan) are by no means limited to that country. Featherbedding such as he describes is the most obvious aspect of Latin American bureaucracy; it has even been known in North American city halls and state capitols and is of course rife in business, from the railroads to the theater. If workers were paid only for a good day's production, our unemployment rolls would be far higher.

Informed Italians have told me that business and industry in that country carry many thousands of workers on their payrolls merely as a form of social insurance—insurance of the Italian *status quo*.

Britain, having lost its political supremacy and feeling the harsh probings of competitive economies, is beginning to see itself as "an over-populated, post-industrial, post-imperial, rainy, lower-middle-class island in the North Sea." [31] Even *The Economist*, commenting on such attempts to block invasion of the countryside, as are becoming more and more necessary in the United States, says of Britain, ". . . If it is true that land (at least in some areas) ought to be rationed, it would be much fairer to deter people by fiscal means from using too much of it, instead of relying on blunt, administrative prohibitions, which bar some people from living there altogether. For example, building plots of more than a certain size (say, one-eighth of an acre) might be surcharged for rating on an ascending scale; anyone who enclosed too many of the green fields of Sweetshire into his own private garden would then have to pay more to the community for them.

"Such a device would not be popular, but it would provide

greater opportunities for mobility. It would bring home the fact that in modern Britain space, quiet and privacy should be regarded as scarce commodities." [32]

England of the green lanes, of the skylark on the Downs and the nightingale in the garden seems destined to become an England of 50 x 100 foot building lots with the song of the blackbird replaced by the sound of the "telly," if its population and its "living standard" continue to "rise."

It is hard for us fortunate Americans, with our relative abundance of resources and space, to visualize how population growth is twisting the day-to-day living of billions of our fellow creatures. Many more white women will be disemboweled in Africa before the decent controls of civilization overtake its racing population growth. Machete-swinging *campesinos*, and stone-throwing universitarians are merely symptoms of the *cultura* of which the Latin Americans once liked to boast but which escapes more and more of them as they outbreed their educational and other civilizing opportunities.

In Britain the "telly" becomes almost as inescapable as the neighbors and the neighbors' children in Japan. Privacy is to be rationed by square feet and pounds, shillings and pence, as the human mass takes over more and more of sheer living space. In most of these countries, as in Scandinavia and the United States, government grows in size, cost and intrusiveness, as people try to cope with growing numbers of people.

But the sheer horror of the rising tidal wave of numbers is still hard to comprehend. It is, perhaps, because I lived with it in a strange and poignant way that I sense so strongly the threat of its impact.

In 1940, while I was doing research on the guano bird colonies of millions of cormorants and pelicans off the coast of Peru, one of the recurrent famines hit. The islands were covered with young birds, each nearly as tall as a year-old child, and, to the unprofessional eye, resembling black-fronted penguins.

As the food supply shrank and the adults had to range farther and farther afield in search of fish, the young became thinner and more vocal. Like human babies, these cried from hunger and now the complaint went on all through the night. I could roughly gauge the success of the adults' fishing by the cries from the two million young.

They were probably suffering also from thirst under the Peruvian desert sun, since the freshly caught fish was their only source of liquid. I would go out on the *pampa* in the morning and be almost knocked down by the horde of downy babies. They would flap their unfledged wings, while they gave their hunger call, at the feet of this strange, uncormorant-like creature who was, withal, vertical and moving.

There was not a thing one could do for them. Day by day there were fewer begging, more staggering about and listlessly drooping. And then more—hundreds of thousands more —of the pitiful, collapsed, downy clumps that were the dead.

When a rare adult returned with food, he would be literally overwhelmed by screeching young. Whether or not he fed his own offspring, or merely those who could best fight their way to him, I could not tell. Finally, perhaps because they were themselves dying, the parent birds simply did not return to the island.

What had been an animated nursery turned into a wide desolation with no sound but the sea and the gulls, and no movement but the scavenging gulls and condors.

Human beings die more stoically. But here was mass death in unforgettable shape and sound. Somehow, ever since, it has been possible to understand more fully the famines of China and India.

Both these countries may well know famine again within the next decade. If the Chinese starve, we shall probably do nothing to help because we disagree with the politics of the tyrants who rule them.

If the Indians starve we shall assuredly try to help them, and the Indians will be lucky if we do not make the situation worse through our well-intentioned meddling.

Ten thousand babies dying in the Indian countryside will not be very different from such a holocaust in the Hudson Valley or Marin County. If we could imagine it more vividly, perhaps we would bring to it a more realistic concern.

There is no excuse for the people of India, Pakistan, China, and parts of Africa, not to remember famine—and fear it again. It is sheer fantasy, on their part, to assume that people in other parts of the world will send them enough food to avert catastrophe.

It is obvious that by failing to check their population growth they are not only diminishing the possibility of a rise in their living standard. They are risking out and out starvation, perhaps for millions.

Yet India, up to the time of writing this book, has—apart from talk—not made more than a modest start toward cutting its birth rate; the establishment of twenty-five hundred clinics in ten years is slow progress. Pakistan has done even less. China deliberately slowed down its birth control campaign. Africa has done less than any of these other areas.

When the pinch comes, when the babies, like the Peruvian cormorants, cry all night from hunger, when death stalks slowly, then quickly through the villages, there will be loud lamentations.

The West will be blamed for not giving more help.

And many in the West will feel a sense of guilt that they have not sent more billions, though they have plenty left undone for their own people, at home.

When the tack on which the underdeveloped peoples are sitting, the tack of too large a population resulting from an "excessive reproductive enthusiasm," has already begun to hurt, is it not time for the governments and the people of the underdeveloped countries to move to a more comfortable seat?

If they insist on maintaining their seat on the tack, they should at least have the good manners not to disturb their neighbors with their complaints.

6

The Great Indian Tragedy

"India faces a crisis of overwhelming gravity . . ." [1]

THE FOOD SITUATION IN A COUNTRY STRUGGLING TO avoid being swept over the brink into starvation has rarely, if ever, been analyzed as well as that of India in a 1959 study sponsored by the Ford Foundation. It was made by a group of outstanding North American technicians, topflight agricultural specialists, and the document's candid recognition of the magnitude of some of the problems is most unusual in an international report. It is perhaps the most honest account of its kind yet produced, and it makes no pretense about what the Indian nation is up against. This is a "blood, sweat and tears" commentary on human ecology. The frankness of the report, which at times is blunt in its criticism, speaks well for the honest understanding developed between the Indian peo-

ple and the Ford Foundation—not to mention the mature re-
sponse of the Indians to such criticism. It is a far cry from the
United Nations' 1949 document, *Mission to Haiti*, which, as a
member of this study group admitted to me, counseled measures that, if adopted, would have left the Haitians in a far
worse situation than the mission found them. The Ford report
is especially striking since the Foundation, like most organizations of its kind, is not given to exaggeration; if anything, it
is apt to lean toward the conservative side.

The Ford report is also notable in emphasizing that "there
are no simple solutions to India's food production problems.
No two or three easy steps can be taken to allay the impending
crisis." [2] The report identifies many of the forces that must be
dealt with, and the controls that must be imposed upon them,
in a highly illuminating way. It reiterates that the "crisis can
and will be prevented." [3]

Does the report protest too much? There are so many possibilities in the Indian tangle for limiting factors to operate
that the obstacles to be overcome are very great indeed.

The experts who drew up the report have given India a
virtual blueprint of an agricultural revolution to be brought
about in seven years' time! Should the revolution fail, a mere
half-dozen years hence, we may see nearly half a billion
people in an agonizing demonstration that Malthus's theories
were basically sound. The results—whether of Indian success
or failure—are sure to be felt far beyond the country's borders
and the consequences could be world-shaking. And since
we, in comfortable, overstuffed America, are part of the
world, what happens during the next half-dozen years in this
subcontinent may be of fateful import to us.

From 1947 to 1958 the population of India grew from 345,-
000,000 to an estimated 398,000,000. During this period, the
rate of infant mortality dropped from more than 130 per
thousand to something under 100—one clue to why India's
population is swelling so rapidly. In the first eleven years of

India's independence, average life expectancy jumped more than a half, from twenty-seven to forty-two years! (It is still not a great deal over half that in the United States and Scandinavia.) Between 1950 and 1955, the population of India had an average growth of about five million per year; from 1955 to 1960, some seven million per year; and it is expected that in the five years ending in 1966, the population will have increased at the rate of ten million per year! This means that by the end of the Third Five Year Plan in 1966, "food will have to be provided for eighty million more people" than when the report was made—a population explosion from 360 million in 1951 to an estimated 480 million by 1966! This expansion is the equivalent of over half the total population of the United States![4]

"The entire nation," the report declares, *"must be made aware of the impending food crisis and steps must be taken to meet it.* Adequate supplies of food may indeed be essential to survival of democracy, because freedom from hunger is a prerequisite to enjoyment of other freedoms."[5]

During the First Five Year Plan the Indians increased their annual food production from a base of 58,000,000 tons of food grains to 65,500,000 tons "quite easily," in part because of emphasis on agricultural production (which was later subordinated to industrial expansion) and with the help of unusually favorable weather.

The Second Five Year Plan set a target of 80,500,000 tons of food grains by 1960-61; but an Indian inquiry in 1957 reported that, according to most of the State Governments, *not more than three-fifths of the targets* under the Second Plan will actually be achieved.

A crop of 100 millon tons a year—assuming that population continues to increase at the projected rates—would permit a slight improvement in the diet of those who are now at bare subsistence levels, "but it would not provide a safety margin for adverse weather nor for reserve stocks needed to stabilize prices and to meet other unforeseen emergencies. A target of 110 million tons is necessary to allow for these contingencies. . . .

"In order to produce 110 million tons of food grains annually by the end of the Third Plan, the rate of production increase must average 8.2 per cent for the next seven years. This rate of increase compares with an annual average of 2.3 per cent from 1949-50 to 1958-59, and an average of 3.2 per cent from 1952-53 to 1958-59. The task is overwhelming. The urgency of an all-out effort is obvious. Adequate resources must be made available to accomplish the job.

"It is clear that the necessity for conserving foreign exchange requires holding imports of food grains to a minimum level, except as imports become available under special exchange programmes . . .

"*A Third Plan target of 110 million tons must be reached if the country is to go forward on its development programme. In fact greatly accelerated expansion of food production is necessary to prevent hunger and possible civil disturbance.*" [6]

The agricultural production team endorsed the statement made by some Indian leaders "that if the food problem is to be solved, the work must be placed on a 'war-footing!' " [7]

In analyzing the Indian food situation and in listing the problems that must be dealt with if the crisis is not to get out of hand, the Ford Foundation report discusses some seventy or more factors.

Of these seventy, only one—climate—can be said to be purely geographic, and not a product of man's culture. (Even climate, in the strictest sense—for example, microclimates and evapo-transpiration rates—has been in no little degree altered by human activities.)

There are few places in India where forests and grasslands have not been profoundly changed by man, and soil and water nearly everywhere show the ravages of man's handiwork. As a result floods roar down river valleys, silt raises their beds, the waters are driven out across fields, towns and cities, and life is disrupted. In the areas of water shortage man has contrived with his "controlled" waters to ruin millions of acres of land. Few landscapes exemplify George Perkins Marsh's *The Earth as Modified by Human Action* as dramatically as does the scarred face of ancient India.

The "multitude" of plant pests and plant diseases that the Ford report discusses are again largely the product of man's improved environments for insects, rusts, viruses, etc. Man has set up nearly ideal conditions for these competitors with human beings, much as the dirty inhabitants of crowded medieval towns set the stage for the Black Death by providing optimum conditions for the rats and lice that carried it. Roughly three-quarters of the processes with which the Ford team was concerned are almost or quite *completely* "cultural"; that is to say, they are *limited* to processes that go on within the nervous system of man, or with artifacts and behavior that are the result of nervous processes, such as money, tools, statistics, religion, social organization, etc. Were the proportions reversed, and three-quarters of the problem to be solved in the realm of the non-human, the prospects of success would seem brighter. We know far more about the behavior of molecules in the soil and in fertilizers than we do about those within the cerebral cortex.

When we recall the caveat of the committee of experts, that solution of the food problem should not be sought in terms of three or four variables or components, but that it must be attacked as an interrelated complex, the task before the Indian people in the next six years is seen to be even more formidable. But it is the very recognition of the interdependence among these various processes, and of the fact that they shape each other—in other words that their relationship is non-additive—that makes the analysis and recommendations so impressive to anyone who is familiar with underdeveloped countries.

This is not an either-or program. It is not developed in terms of economics *or* education *or* science *or* technology *or* work on the land; it is all of these things at once. It is the kind of analysis on which the Point Four Program concept should have been based when it was first formulated. Every underdeveloped country is unique but all share to some degree such problems as have been enumerated for India, and the structure of the solution of these problems will be somewhat similar from country to country.

Figure II, based largely on the processes the Ford report considers indispensable to the increase of food production, shows *some* of the relationships. There would not be room for all of them on a small diagram, and it is not certain that all of them could be foreseen. Only about one-half of the factors enumerated in the Ford report are listed.

One of the needs stressed over and over again in the Ford report is research. It is clear that much of the recommended program must, in the absence of such research, consist of varying degrees of guesswork. This research, alone, involves a number of goods and services that may present complicated and expensive problems. Laboratories, research institutes, and field stations will be required to give both natural and social scientists places to work. Libraries of books and periodicals, both in short supply in India, will be indispensable. Capital will be required, as in almost every phase of the agricultural development program, and this will also include a supply of foreign exchange for books, equipment and foreign travel.

Investigators who are sufficiently trained so they may be expected to come up with an approximation of the "right" answers will, of course, be the base on which a research program must be built. India possesses outstanding scientists but only a small fraction of the numbers that would be needed to guide such a program as the Ford Foundation has suggested, especially if it is to make up, in the short space of seven years, the 28,000,000 ton annual grain shortage.

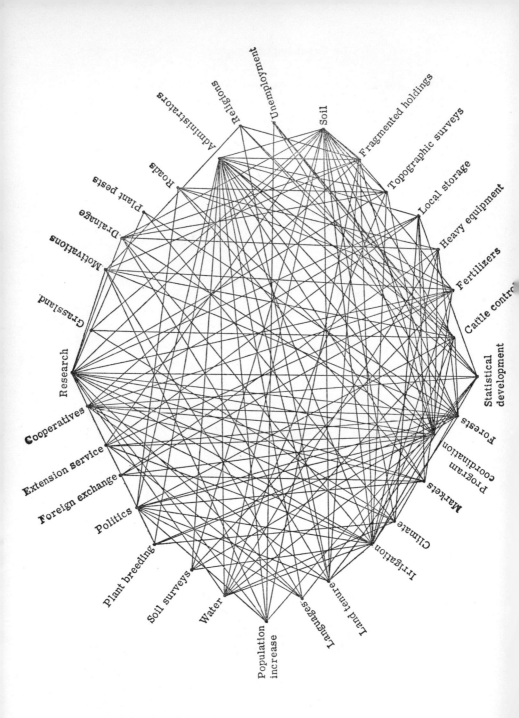

Unemployment
Religions
Administrators
Soil
Fragmented holdings
Roads
Topographic surveys
Plant pests
Local storage
Drainage
Heavy equipment
Motivations
Fertilizers
Grassland
Cattle control
Research
Statistical development
Cooperatives
Forests
Extension service
Program coordination
Foreign exchange
Markets
Politics
Climate
Plant breeding
Irrigation
Soil surveys
Land tenure
Water
Languages
Population increase

FIGURE 2. The Ford Foundation team of agricultural experts emphasized that "there are no simple solutions to India's food production problems. No two or three easy steps can be taken to allay the impending crisis." Of the seventy-odd factors listed by the team as components in the Indian food revolution, this diagram shows less than half; and of the interrelationships among these factors, only a part are suggested. The Ford report stresses fertilizers and water as especially important. To make use of the former will involve (among other things) research, roads, capital, fabrication (not shown on diagram), soil surveys, extension services to provide education, administrators, program co-ordinators, publications, etc., and substantial adjustments will have to be made to climate, soils, rainfall, etc. If these factors are ignored or neglected the potential value of the fertilizers will be reduced to a greater or lesser degree. Without more water available when it is needed, to take an especially important example, fertilizers will help relatively little and come at a much higher cost. Et cetera!

This country of 380,000,000 people has thirty-eight universities that are at present forced to turn away many thousands of students for lack of facilities. And yet, despite the shortage of educational opportunities there are far more university graduates than there are jobs for them to fill! A recent survey showed that of 578 students who returned in 1959 from study abroad, 47 per cent with graduate degrees had no jobs.[8]

Even down-to-earth basic programs, such as providing better water supplies, have ramifications that range from the small peasant farm in the Punjab to the halls of the United States Congress.

Improved water facilities are the most important part of the plan drawn up by the Ford team, since some 80 per cent of the rain received by most of India falls during a short four months. For the balance of the year a great deal of the country is subject to scorching winds and burning rays of the tropical sun that combine to turn much of the land into something like a vast ceramic crust not dissimilar to the *tepetate* that abuse of the land has left behind in much of Latin America.

Simple tube-well irrigation has brought about crop increases of 45 to 100 per cent in India. Without irrigation, optimum use of water is impossible. Irrigation itself, however, creates complications. It requires, for example, that there be adequate drainage to avoid waterlogging of soils and excessive concentration of salts in the irrigated farm lands. It is said that some three million acres have gone out of cultivation in the Punjab alone from this cause.

Irrigation is inescapably, among other things, an engineering problem. The rapid spread of irrigation cannot take place without the education of engineers and surveyors.

But before the engineer can do his job, it is almost indispensable that new land tenure systems be worked out. The average family farm in India amounts to only 5.3 acres and is often so broken up as to make any efficient layout of irrigation ditches impossible. "The general pattern of field formation is irregular. It has grown as population has grown. There has hardly been any change ever since the first settlement operations that took place some centuries ago. As a result of such irregular configuration of culturable plots, the water courses have to follow tortuous courses and to suffer many bends and kinks. The water from the outlet head has to traverse a longer distance than what would be necessary, had the fields been formed in proper geometrical formations. Besides, the fields are not leveled up, which results in more water getting accumulated in one part of the field than in the other." [9]

Soil conservation practices are also indispensable in water management to increase yields, keep the soil from being washed away and preventing the siltation of reservoirs. This again calls for at least simple engineering practices. There are also involved difficulties connected with what the report calls "water conveyance," especially to reduce the loss of water through seepage.

Irrigation farming is a very different operation from non-irrigation farming and not only will it be necessary to teach this through a system of agricultural extension agents, in the view of the Ford team, but the progress of the whole irrigation program must also be speeded up by establishing demonstration areas to show the advantages the farmer will gain through these new procedures. Someone will have to teach the teachers and this will probably require the development of agricultural schools or some substitute for them.

The difficulties of water application in most Indian villages, the report emphasizes, are "enormous." In many of the irrigated areas "water is available for more than one crop per year. Yet a recent survey has shown that only about 12 per cent of the land under irrigation has more than one irrigated crop grown per year. Even on the one irrigated crop, the use of adequate fertilizer and good seed are the exceptions rather than the rule." [10]

The report repeatedly drives home the importance of concentrating early efforts in areas that will bring the greatest success; it emphasizes and re-emphasizes that the water should be combined with fertilizer, improved seeds, etc., without the use of which maximum advantage will not be taken of the water when it *is* made available.

At the present time India uses relatively minute amounts of fertilizer per acre, only 1/130th of the nitrogenous fertilizer used per acre in Japan, and a little less than 1/500th of the phosphate.[11] Even at that low figure the national supply is said to be inadequate to meet the demand. There will have to be an expansion of manufacture and importation of fertilizers, along with crop and soil studies to determine proper mixtures, times of application, etc.; and teaching facilities will have to be made available throughout the hundreds of thousands of Indian villages so that farmers will know what fertilizer to use and where and when to use it.

The Foundation report recommends that there be set up a governmental agency for the co-ordination and improvement of "drainage ways," with virtual police power to manage water resources. This recommendation implies the development of a corps of administrators, engineers and supervisors at various levels from the national to the village, etc. Most of these functionaries will also have to be trained, and their operation will have to be fitted into the bureaucratic hierarchy. To anyone who has watched the pulling and hauling when comparable innovations have been attempted in our own Departments of State, Defense, and Agriculture, a simple, easy reorganization of this sort would be a considerable surprise.

India is a polyglot country, in which some 80 per cent of the people can neither read nor write, and out of this situation will grow the need to develop technicians to work in a

dozen or more languages, and to present ideas and material
in such a way as to get them across to the nonliterate.

In a sense, this is comparable to the problem we have faced
for many decades, in our own southern states, of trying to win
the support of the country folk in the prevention and control
of forest fires. We have made considerable progress, though
woods-burning is far from a thing of the past. A similar
type of approach to the Indian problem—through a search
for "natural leaders," and enlistment of their understanding
and support—is recommended by the Ford team for India. It
will be interesting to see whether this technique, originally
developed for the United States Forest Service, will be effective in a totally different culture, complicated far beyond
anything we have here by such possible points of friction as
caste and religious conflicts.

The fertilizers the Ford team considers indispensable if the
production target is to be reached in time will, of course, have
to be distributed over an area nearly one-third as large as
the United States. Highways and railroads are totally inadequate. Indeed, the Ford team even recommends the construction of farm-to-market roads in order that farmers may sell
their products. Must this, too, be done if those missing tons are
to be found by 1966?

"If India's food production increases no faster than present rates," says the report, at another point, *"the gap between
supplies and target will be 28 million tons by 1965-66.* This
will be about 25 per cent shortfall in term of need. *No conceivable programme of imports or rationing can meet a
crisis of this magnitude."* The italics are those of the Ford
Team. So, too, is the expressed urgency. It is an urgency so
rare as to be almost, if not quite, unique in a report of this
kind.

Yet with all its urgency, the report leaves us without even
tentative answers to some important and closely related questions of which the Indians are certainly aware and that con-

cern us almost as much as that the food development plan
should succeed. This is not to diminish, in any way, the stature of the report. It had to be prepared in a hurry, because
the team of experts were almost all on leave from responsible
posts at home; and because in the food "war" that must be
won within eighty-four months, every lost week is almost
equal to a lost battle.

A major shortcoming in the report is the absence of a price
tag. How many billions of rupees—or billions of dollars, for
that matter—are going to be needed to buy and build the
arms that India will have to have to win this peaceful war?
What of the cost of research and of training both scientists
and technicians to cope with the rising flood of ten million
more hungry human beings every year?

What of allies? As we discovered in two world wars and
Korea, conflicts cannot, unfortunately, be won by money
alone. Men and women are going to be needed. Where, and
how, are they to be found? In the United States?

In the 1940's Americans were sharply criticized—with no
little justification—in the press of Colombia. I remember discussing the matter with Dr. Baldomero Sanín Cano, known
and beloved in his own country as "the sage of Popayán." He
looked like a character out of *Pickwick Papers* and spoke an
almost Dickensian English. The United States has never had a
more appreciative and admiring friend in South America.

"The trouble is," he said, "that we do not have a chance to
know you Americans at home, where we can see your good
family life; understand your outpouring of generosity; know
your culture at first hand; and, above all, learn to realize that
even though you sometimes lack the outward forms of politeness, yours is a courtesy based on consideration for the other
person that is more genuine and goes far deeper than our almost ritual forms.

"Why you leave these characteristics at home or at least
conceal them abroad, I don't know. But so many of your visi-

tors to Colombia give a completely opposite impression. I sometimes think you should build a six-foot fence around your country and stay inside it."

I felt no disposition to argue with him since I had seen an appalling amount of bad manners, all over South America, on the part of my compatriots. The reasons are often pitiable, rather than deserving of condemnation, and need not be discussed here; but the phenomenon has persisted since long before the days of *The Ugly American* down to the present. One has only to watch an American mob from a cruise ship trooping through Bombay or New Delhi to realize what the United States is up against.

Gaucheness, bad taste and bad manners are not characteristic of all Americans abroad, nor are they limited to any group. I have seen State Department people who were as offensive as some missionaries, and many a traveler with an official passport whose obvious sense of superiority must have curdled the stomach fluids of the "natives." The public health experts, perhaps because they have been trained to deal with masses of people, have one of the best records. Our business men have improved. And I recently lunched with a missionary who was going to Asia, as nearly as I could find out, primarily to try to make amends for the arrogance of his predecessors toward the worshippers of the local gods.

India is going to need a great deal of technical help long before she can possibly train her own experts. Where there are scores or a few hundreds of field workers from abroad, thousands will have to be found. They will need not only skillful ways with water, and soil, and seeds but even more with people. Like a foot soldier going into battle, they must be prepared to leave the "American standard of living" behind. One cannot drive into an Indian village in a bright blue Chevrolet and expect to have much success in establishing rapport with the *panchayat*.

Can we, in our nation of 180,000,000 find enough men and

women of ability, training, vision and dedication to help another nation of 480,000,000 escape disaster?

One American general, retiring from a position of command in Korea, was quoted as saying that if he had it to do over again he would permit no private cars among his officers and civilian staff. Can we even find enough Americans who will be willing to walk? This may seem like a ridiculously simplified qualification; but it could be critical in establishing communication that *may* make it possible to get the job done. In Latin America the Yankee agronomist who would go out into the fields and get his boots muddy often did more for relations among our peoples than the American Ambassador.

In foreign aid, as in two or three other fields, the Russians seem to have some real advantages. They start from a lower material living standard, and thus are able to accept that of the underdeveloped country more readily than we. They are more highly disciplined, and because they lack the wide choice of careers that "full employment" offers even the incompetent American, are probably glad to have a chance to prove themselves under rigorous conditions. Few of them aspire to anything like Montclair or San Mateo, and the 8:13. They learn to "dominate" foreign languages as a matter of course and arrive at their posts speaking Hindi, Gujerati, or whatever is necessary. (It is reported that competence in common Western languages has improved in our Foreign Service since the war; but even here, and still more among obscure tongues, we still lag seriously behind the Communists.) The problem of human resources to help India save herself is a major one, and can probably be solved only if we are willing to accept her feeling that this is a war and a desperate one. Certainly this sentiment seemed to be deeply shared by the Ford Foundation team.

There is, in some quarters, strong sentiment for carrying out such programs through the United Nations and its agen-

cies. This cannot be done in the case of India because the need
is so great and so pressing. Resources of men and money that
would seem totally disproportionate in the commonwealth of
nations must be poured into India if the disaster is to be
averted. Enough help for India may well result in reducing
aid elsewhere, simply because cash, equipment, men and materials are limited. India must, in terms of our aid, become a
"most favored nation." India must become our ally—not in
abandoning her neutralist position to which, as a free nation,
she is entitled—but in the war for freedom and democracy
for her own people.

India cannot solve her problems—one might say any of
her problems—solely in terms of food. The vast pool of unemployed, including the college graduates, remains. If jobs are
to be found for them—they will not starve indefinitely with
equanimity—there will have to be industrial development. The
millions of workers on the land can be occupied only a few
months a year. Some way must be found of helping them
to get jobs. The Ford team recommends public works projects: terracing, irrigating, and road building that will contribute to the expansion of food production. This program which
will necessitate less capital per worker than development of
heavy industry, and, far from being a WPA make-work project, will help to put a solid base under the food production
program, should probably have high priority, but it is not
going to be enough. As numbers grow, the need will grow.

What of 1976—1986—1996?

The Indian population is going to continue to explode (unless falling living standards reverse the trend in mortality
rates, which have been dropping rapidly) and even should
the 28,000,000-ton food gap be closed by 1966, the desperate
need for even greater production is going to hang like a
storm cloud over India for decades, unless still another mighty
force is put under governance—the high birth rate. And on
this incontestable need, which has been officially recognized

by the Indian government, the Ford team study is strangely silent.

It says, merely, "Although there is considerable emphasis on family planning in India, no appreciable slowing down of population growth may be expected during the Third Plan period." [12] No evidence is provided to support this opinion, and at least one member of the team has privately expressed himself as believing there is almost no hope of avoiding famine unless population growth is retarded. It is inconceivable that other members of the group should not agree that it would be easier in India to provide food for 400,000,000 than for 480,000,000!

The motto of most planners seems to be, almost without exception, "Millions for tribute—not one cent for defense!" Billions of rupees and of dollars are actually earmarked for feeding the voracious population yet to be born; India has appropriated only some two million dollars a year for defense against their rising numbers, a minute fraction of the larger sums. It is, as Sir Julian Huxley has pointed out, only a small part of what is being spent for the control of a single disease, malaria.[13]

Yet from the Prime Minister down to simple peasant women, there is abundant evidence that large numbers of the Indian people have a strong desire to keep their families small.

Lt. Col. B. L. Raina, the Army surgeon who is in charge of the national population control project, speaks in the words of the Ford team when he says, "This is now war." [14]

This is recognized by some leading Indians, including Prime Minister Nehru, as another war they cannot afford to lose. "Population control will not solve all our problems," he has stated, "but other problems will not be solved without it."

Yet there seems to be a general assumption that it is easier (and cheaper) to get the mass of people in India to revolutionize their farming practices than to get them to use contraceptives! Nothing like the amount of thought and effort has gone into developing motivations for family planning as for accepting the new way of life projected by the agronomists, although the Ford Foundation is sponsoring a $300,-000 study of birth-control motivations and motivation techniques. Perhaps this approach is based on sound reasoning, but it remains unproven. A condom is much simpler to manage than an irrigation ditch, and capital required to avoid the creation of another hungry human being is certainly much less than the capital that will be needed to support him decently after he is born.

Even many Planned Parenthood advocates take a defeatist attitude toward the likelihood of success, and postpone hope of significant results until the day of the oral contraceptive. The plain fact of the matter is, as the Ford report makes abundantly clear, there is not time to wait!

The Swedes had indisputable, though limited, control over their birth rates as early as the middle of the eighteenth century; during depressions and after bad harvests birth rates showed marked declines.[15] They also dropped elsewhere in Europe, long before modern contraceptives became available.

As has been said, there is a general disposition favorable to birth limitation in India, which is more fortunate than the West in two respects. It seems free, to a considerable degree, from the puritanical attitudes that make sex a cryptic subject that can be discussed only in an atmosphere of guilt. At the First International Planned Parenthood Conference in Bombay in 1952, long counters displayed contraceptives as casually as though they had been fruits and vegetables. (In Japan, in 1955, when the International Conference was held in a Masonic Hall, the display had to be restricted because of protests, not from Japanese, but from an American women's club!) Furthermore, and of considerable importance, there is virtually no religious opposition to birth control in India, nor is there a militant minority threatening economic and political hatchet-work against those who advocate birth control and make it available to those who need it. By contrast, political warfare is carried out in many parts of India against those who advocate the cow slaughter that could so measurably help expand food production! (It is somewhat ironic that the Ford report suggests progressively higher taxes on cattle as a possible means of reducing their numbers. Indians and Japanese have suggested that similar taxation patterns be applied to children, especially after the second.)

This is one country in which limitation of the human population, provided it is given equal emphasis, may prove as feasible an answer to a desperate dilemma as industrial and agricultural development combined.

And if India could be flooded with tens of millions of dollars of simple, cheap contraceptives, such as condoms and foam tablets, the effect on the birth rate might well surprise population forecasters who have, after all, been mistaken before!

This is not to suggest that population control is a substitute for development. Both are obviously needed, and it seems most regrettable that some of the most perceptive exponents of increasing production have not recognized the equal importance of decreasing reproduction.

Why is the case of India so desperately important?

One finds the answer in the faces of the Indian people. As one travels through the countryside there is a haunting sense of being with people who have rarely, if ever, had enough to eat. The sunken cheeks and hollow eyes of the adults, the swollen bellies of the babies, bespeak too little food and the wrong kind. There seem to be many elderly people about, but the greater number of them are old at forty and fifty, even in their thirties. There are hosts of children who, a few short years ago, would have died in infancy.

Should there be the "shortfall" of 28,000,000 tons of food grain by 1966, combined with monsoon failure, famine could run through this land like a prairie fire, a worse famine, possibly, than any history has known. And if it does not come in 1966 it could be far worse ten years later, unless population growth has been slowed down. It is almost overwhelming to consider the agony this half-billion people might have to endure. As the Ford team emphasizes, "No conceivable programme of imports or rationing can meet a crisis of this magnitude." Simple humanity demands every possible help for the Indian people.

And if simple humanity is not enough, an adequate aid program which is going to make heavy demands on us Americans, must be offered in the interest of the West.

India is the great bastion of democracy in Asia. It is the obvious counterfoil to Red China. Despite almost incredibly stupid political strategy, Red China's progress in material development undoubtedly has a powerful appeal to the politically "uncommitted" third of the world's population. They are ill informed and misinformed. They have few sound bases for judging what happens in Mao Tse-tung's domain. If Mao reaches only half his goals, and if five million people starve to death in India—or ten million—it will be difficult for the uncommitted and uninformed to reach any other conclusion than that Communism is superior.

Within India itself, where the young government would need more hands than Vishnu to cope with its manifold problems, it is doubtful if even the leadership of Prime Minister Nehru could survive a major famine. And Nehru is not a young man. The Indian people with their religious respect for the individual that transcends much of the usual downgrading of the individual by overpopulation, would probably turn not so much toward Communism (which Mao is putting in the worst possible light) as away from the light that failed. If democracy cannot even feed them, how can they have faith in democracy? To quote the Ford team again: *"If elementary wants, such as food and clothing, are not satisfied, other freedoms may be sacrificed for the promise of food enough."* The italics are theirs.

India's war for food and population control is our war—America's—along with that of the rest of the West. The fate of India, and therefore of democracy, may be decided quite as definitely in the Congress of the United States as in India's Lokh Sahba. Our Marshall Plan was, on the whole, successful (at least over the short period) because it was adequate, and because it was wisely carried out, both by the United States and most of the recipients. But the problems that made the Marshall Plan necessary were simple in comparison with those of India. The Marshall Plan countries, ravaged though they had been by war, possessed great resources of trained men and women. Their cultural level showed them the road ahead. In comparison, India must cope with vast gaps and the thinest of resources to fill them.

The total appropriations for the European recovery program from 1948 through June of 1952 were $13.15 billion.[16] Would it not be worth as much to save India? Can people be found to back up the dollars? Money itself will not be enough.

This is not a war that will be won at the last moment. Sometime within the next few years, India may reach a breaking point, when she will collapse with little hope of recovery. We should be less than intelligent if we willingly or carelessly let this happen. The longer we improvise, the longer we scatter our largesse instead of concentrating it where it will be really effective, the longer we refuse to face up to the indisputable facts of raging population growth, the less chance we shall have of success.

India is a calculated risk. The task is so great we might fail in spite of our mightiest efforts. And if we do we shall, of course, share the onus of the failure. But that India will fall without western help seems so probable that we can scarcely refuse to seize the responsibility and the opportunity.

This assumes, of course, that India wants help and that we shall at all times have to give it on terms that India will want. We are somewhat in the position of France, holding out a helping hand to the young American Republic. It is to be hoped that the Indians would understand it in that light. It is to be hoped our Congress and our State Department would understand it in that light—not to mention the development troops that must be sent to the field. For this is a problem sunk deep in human potentialities and limitations, and if it is to be solved anywhere it will be in the minds of men.

The most unfortunate action we could take would be in-action.

7

The Ethics of Parenthood—1960

WHAT RIGHT HAVE YOU TO HAVE A CHILD?

This is a direct question to every reader of this book who is physically able to reproduce himself or herself, or who is likely to be, within the next few years. It is a question that should be kept before the world's people.

It is a question that has been asked far too seldom. Indeed, the "right" to have children has been so uncritically accepted that various schools of busybodies who make a career of telling people what they are "morally" bound to do, have harped on man's *obligation* to reproduce himself. Their certainties have often been compounded by their own feelings of guilt about sex, with a resultant punitive attitude. If you enjoy sex, then you must pay for it!

What the imposition of life on the child may cost him seems to have been given little thought. Western supernaturalists have found for it a strange justification in an afterlife that may quite as probably condemn the soul (for which they are providing the body) to hell as to heaven, particularly if the child is born into a hell on earth; and this has been the lot of countless millions of children throughout history. (The influential members of the environmentalist school, convinced that most forms of human delinquency can be obviated by improved housing, economic conditions, etc., clearly accept the hell-on-earth-to-hell-hereafter probability, at least so far as they accept a Judgment Seat and post-mortem existence.)

Elaborate means of escape have sometimes been provided in the next world (if not in this one) with often a tacit or stipulated agreement that the escape would be available to relatively few—those who have participated in some limited sort of ritual. The production, by parents, of the pre-damned may have troubled more consciences than we have recognized; this aspect of human behavior would seem to call for more exploration than has yet been given it.

Certainly, the right of the child to be born or not to be born has been little weighed until very recent times. Even now, as a new study shows, some parents maintain that it is God that sends children,[1] as insurance men blame earthquakes on Him and, therefore, shrug off responsibility.

The answer to the question that opens this chapter will be far from simple, but it may be clearer and more readily found if it is sought in terms of two relationships: with the child itself, and with the total environment (not limited only to other people) in which the child will live.

It is important, before considering the question at all to remember that *not* being born will make absolutely no difference to the child. It does not exist. It cannot miss anything— love, pleasure, happiness or joy. Until the ovum is fertilized by the sperm there is no life, no sentience, no possibility of deprivation. By failing to have a child we do it no harm. It is not. So far as the *child* is concerned any qualms, conscious or subconscious, we may feel about not having it are baseless. We are not depriving "it" of anything. There is no "it." Had I never been born, it would not have made the least difference to me.

To create this "it," to bring it into the world, is an act of the greatest responsibility any human being can incur. The responsibility is even greater than taking life, for the dead human being is, again, nothing, a mass of decaying organic matter, a handful of dust. After he is dead nothing can matter to him, as Cicero pointed out, any more than it could before he was conceived. ("Rightness" and "wrongness" are not under discussion here—merely the responsibility we incur, the impact on another human being, when we give or take life.)

Recognizing, then, that we deprive no child, no human being, of anything by not having it, should we not be reasonably confident before we create it that we can give it a good enough life so that it will be glad it was born—in middle and old age, as well as in youth? Unless we feel such confidence, the act of begetting is the supreme human selfishness.

It is obvious from the misery that stalks the earth that millions of parents were either mistaken about the future of their children or, much more likely, thoughtless or guilty of this selfishness. The "lives of quiet desperation" that Thoreau postulated may possibly not afflict most men, but millions who endure such lives would not carry their burden had it not been for the selfish begetting by their parents.

One thinks of peasants starving in Haiti and China, the millions of trachoma-blinded victims born into filth and disease from Brazil to New Guinea,[2] tubercular southern Italians coughing out their lungs in damp caves.

But one need not go so far afield.

Thousands, tens of thousands, of children born every year in the United States should, solely for their own sakes, never have seen the light of day. There are the illegitimates, around two hundred thousand of them every year. Some are adopted by couples who cannot have children of their own; but most grow up in such a cloaca of poverty, ignorance, crime, and fright, that a vicious circle perpetuates itself—in part through more illegitimacy. The crime is not the children's but they are punished for it.

There are hundreds of thousands of others, technically legitimate since their parents have engaged in some sort of marriage ritual, but whose birth is as much of a crime against them as it is against the bastards.

There are the unwanted, whose parents were too ignorant, too superstitious, too stupid or too irresponsible to see that children were not born. They are rejected, often uncared for, perhaps only partially supported by their parents economically and often not at all emotionally. Many of them are grossly neglected or even abandoned; social workers tell me it is no unusual thing for the parents who brought them into the world (especially the mother) to try to give them away. The father often simply disappears.

From among these children come juvenile delinquents, the highly neurotic and eventually the criminal. (Not all such social pathology originates in this group, of course, nor do all members of it end up in overt difficulty, but it makes a highly disproportionate contribution to the numbers of our trouble makers. A New York City study, as noted before, showed that the "hard-core problem family" had something like four times the number of children of the normal New York family.)

It is obvious that unskilled workers in the United States, often not speaking English, will have inadequate incomes and that anything more than a small number of children in their families becomes excessive. Even with much subsidized housing they suffer from serious overcrowding. As I have said, both father and mother must often work and thus cannot maintain a home. Theirs are the latchkey kids. In the argot, they lack "supportive affection" and if we may believe the Freudian dogma of infant damnation (with salvation possible only at $25 an hour), they have little hope indeed. "Society," which presumably means the rest of us, is blamed for their plight. Their parents, who threw them into the arena, seem not only to be exculpated but through various social and welfare services to be encouraged to impose life on more and more children. The right of the *child* not to be born seems to move neither the social worker nor the priest.

As is pointed out elsewhere, it is forecast that by 1965 one-half of all children born in New York City will be born in indigent families. Should not a fundamental right of the child be that it should not start life as a pauper, dependent on charity?

It is not only the poor who, without justification, force life on helpless offspring. Some 140,000 defective children are born in the United States every year, often as the result of calculated risks on the part of their parents. In some cases these risks are genetic; couples will have a family in spite of knowing that they carry crippling genes, even after the birth of a defective child. An attack of rubella will be ignored. In the backwoods of Maine and the South and undoubtedly of many other parts of the country, one may see whole families living in squalor, most of them obviously subnormal. Yet the parents are not only permitted to bring these children into the world at will; they are encouraged to do so by one sort or another of government assistance. The Societies for Prevention of Cruelty to Children back away from this difficult problem just as humane societies studiously avoid seeing the cruelty of blood sports or of trapping. After all, neither the crippled ducks nor the crippled children can effectively protest!

The unwanted child exists, of course, not only among the poor. The rejected and unloved are all too common throughout various strata of our society, as any school psychologist (who is usually employed largely to cope with the unwanted and rejected) can bear witness. The café society behavior that catches the attention of the columnists and the tabloids is, probably, often of similar etiology. The reasons why parents bring such children into the world are complicated, but are likely to have little relevance to the considered future welfare of the child itself.

The simplest, and undoubtedly the commonest, reason is sexual satisfaction. This is one of the strongest biological drives and one that is least likely to be controlled. Fortunately, now that contraception has made it possible to separate the sex act and reproduction, the probability that intercourse will be followed by conception can be greatly reduced. There are psychoanalysts who seem not to separate the reproductive drives and the need for sexual satisfaction which is, in itself, a far more complex process than Kinsey recognized, ranging as it does from masturbation to the most complex fulfillment of romantic love. One of the most noted New York psychiatrists (a man) maintains that at every intercourse a woman is hoping to be impregnated. Another analyst of international stature flatly states, "There can be no doubt that the immediate instinctive urgency of the sexual desire relates to the sexual act (in one or another of its various possible forms) rather than to reproduction . . . [it] is a matter on which . . . we have still comparatively little knowledge." [3]

There are many other reasons why so little thought is given to the right of the child *not* to be born. They may go far back in time to the aeons when life expectancy was a couple of decades or less,[4] and fifty or sixty children needed to be born every year for every thousand of the population, if the normal death rate was to be balanced; our understandings, and especially our misunderstandings, about human reproduction have roots that are tens of centuries old. During these millennia, beliefs were developed that were sound for their time but have no relevance to the twentieth century. The great burden of superstitions that many of us, like dung beetles, roll before us, was acquired during those thousands of years when not only the matrix of human existence but the existence itself were profoundly different from those in today's world.

In those far-gone days, it should be remembered, prior to the Christian era, there were probably not over 200 to 300 million people in the world, the equivalent of four to six years' increase today[5]; there was safety in numbers, not only as a guarantee of carrying on the race but for protection against human and wild animal attacks. The continuity of the family and even the rearing of the children depended on production of many offspring who, as they grew up, could share in caring for the family even though the mother should die. Anyone who has lived in outlying parts of underdeveloped countries has seen this mechanism in operation today. (One reason so many American mothers, like the cuckoo and the cowbird, transfer the responsibility for rearing their young to the nursery school, kindergarten, school, camp, etc., as early and as many hours a week as possible, is undoubtedly that there are not other children about to share the burden of child rearing. One can sympathize with apartment-dwelling women subjected to the eroding impact of the young sixteen hours every day!)

The idea that there is "safety in numbers" or that the more people there are, the better, dies hard. It has survived into the contemporary credo of many of our economists, not to mention our businessmen, who seem to think that we can copulate ourselves into greater and greater prosperity. One of the problems of today's worker in Planned Parenthood is to make the businessman understand that the economy will be better off with less people living at a higher living standard, and with smaller numbers of children born to those who cannot adequately take care of them and who must parasitize their fellow citizens. A recent Congressional hearing brought out the fact that some thirty million children were living in families with less than $4,000 a year income. It is these families, one might reasonably assume, that could scarcely justify bringing more than one, two or three children into the world, if only for the sake of the children. (Whether or not such families have a right to impose the cost of the care of their children on their fellow citizens, and whether we have an obligation to subsidize their reproduction, will be discussed later.)

That very often a child is not wanted is evidenced by long histories of exposure and other means of infanticide; abortion, which certainly runs to millions a year; by a large number of "shotgun weddings"; and by the generality of birth control among people who know about it and have it easily available.

In a classic essay[6] J.C. Flugel, the British psychologist, has discussed the motives, chiefly unconscious, of people opposed to birth control. These give many clues to why people have children who, if only for their own sakes, should never have been brought into the world.

Freud, according to Flugel, drew attention to the resistance to the ideas of Darwin as a "blow to human Narcissism involved in the recognition of the fact that human life is essentially of the same nature, and is subject to the same conditions, as that of lower animals." *On the Origin of Species* raised the greatest storm of the nineteenth century in forcing man to recognize that he was not "a special creation at the hands of Divinity and to admit that he was of the same descent as his humbler brethren." It is also "unpleasant for him to realize that he is still subject to the same biological laws which control the destiny of the other animals; especially since these laws reveal the existence of an ever-present danger to human life, which it would be much more agreeable to overlook."[7] Even today some of our most intelligent men and women, including those with considerable scientific training, tend to refuse to look at the consequences of a major war or even a major world-wide depression, in terms of

what they would do to hundreds of millions of human beings. Harrison Brown[8] has been one of the rare scientists to
point out the catastrophic and *probably permanent* effects of
an atomic holocaust; and Sir Charles Galton Darwin[9] forecasts a similar return to subsistence peasant living as a result
of what he appears to regard as the inevitable proliferation
of human millions. For these two, there are thousands, especially among the technologists, who continue to insist, "It
can't happen here."

The results of natural selection are rejected by the technologists in the belief that medication, food additives, and the
application of varying social techniques, will somehow deal
effectively with increasing numbers of the unfit; the *facts* of
natural selection, and the struggle for existence, prorogued
though they have temporarily been among a relatively small
segment of the human race, are ignored with an amazing
credulousness that somehow "everything will come out all
right." This is especially characteristic of Americans and he
who puts the belief in question is almost automatically a
"pessimist."

A second factor pointed out by Flugel is "the unwillingness
of men to abandon a certain childlike attitude in virtue of
which they are prone to believe that all their needs will be
provided for without the necessity for forethought or effort
on their own part." Pope John, who would seem never to have
visited southern Italy, in 1959 adjured women not to worry
about having large families since, "There is always the grace
of the Lord. . . ." [10] At a supposedly more sophisticated level,
especially among overfed Americans, we find an expressed
confidence that what in previous centuries we thought the
good Lord would do, "Society" can now do. This leads to
complicated rationalizations and rituals, such as printing a
little more paper money each year, that to the unbeliever are
as fantastic as invoking the assistance of a medieval saint
through the intercession of what is supposed to have been his

clothing or a toe bone. (If this interpretation seems extreme, try asking proponents of a "little more inflation," what will happen to society if we do not accept their particular magic.) At a more naïve level, we find the serene confidence of the slum-dwelling woman with six children who is confident that "the Welfare" will provide.

To quote Flugel again: "The so-frequently expressed blind confidence in the forthcoming of adequate sustenance for human populations, no matter how fast they multiply, represents a regression to an infantile level of thought and feeling. . . . Any attempt to overcome this confidence and to make an unbiased scrutiny of the actual relationship between mouths and food . . . [is] being opposed with an energy that derives its force from a dim realization of the fact that such a scrutiny would threaten with destruction the pious and pleasing illusions which have been built up around this subject."

The high value placed on fertility and virility seems to inflict on large numbers of men and women a sense of inadequacy in the absence of visible signs of their inward, sexual potency. Among certain ethnic groups women feel that they gain much prestige by frequent and even constant pregnancies (let the Devil take care of the hindmost child!). The *machismo* so much talked about in the southern part of our hemisphere leads one to suspect a very general sense of sexual inadequacy among males; the Latin American doth boast too much, and "proves" his virility by large numbers of offspring. A New York tobacconist advertises post-partum cigars each of which carries the legend: "Call me mister!" Flugel comments on the continued enjoyment of phallic symbolism, even in a society where it is suppressed, and on our somewhat morbid horror or disgust at anything that threatens the existence or activity of the sexual organs, for example, castration or impotence. In further support of this opinion he says: "These tendencies are in reality derived from the psychic sources [as] is shown by the fact that those who extol most lavishly the benefits of a high birth rate and who exhibit most alarm at the voluntary control of birth (which they are fond of designating 'race suicide') are to be found chiefly among elderly persons (whose sexual power has departed or is declining) or else among confirmed bachelors, celibate priests or unmarried women."

There is a great deal of out-and-out breeding of slave labor in many societies, both to help with farming and herding and as a social security system for the parents' old age. These are the usual excuses given for large families in poor, underdeveloped countries. The ethics of creating such domestic chattels, often to endure lives of misery if they do not suffer early—and probably painful—death, has so far as I know not been called into question. It is hard to see how the practice could be justified, except on "supernatural" grounds.

Children are often "wanted" and conceived for other reasons that have no relationship with their own welfare—to get a husband, to hold a husband, to hold a wife—or because having a large family is "the thing to do." Any psychiatrist can suggest a dozen more.

Finally—although far from completely—sex is taboo to such a degree in our society that people will often run the risk of conceiving a child, either within or without marriage, rather than "cold-bloodedly" adjust a contraceptive. This taboo is so widespread that it even tends to deter men and women from purchasing contraceptives and perhaps explains the reluctance that is well known among doctors to provide the means of conception control. At the Planned Parenthood Federation of America we receive many letters saying: "My doctor tells me I must have no more children—but he doesn't tell me how to keep from having them."

Whichever may be the explanation, the fact remains that every year, millions of children, perhaps tens of millions of children, are born into a harsh and destructive existence that should never have been imposed upon them; and the fact also remains that although the parents may place the blame for this on God, it would never have happened without their own acts. Theirs is the responsibility and theirs is the blame (to the extent that we can accept free will and with it the responsibility for our own acts) for the misery into which the child is born. Clergymen have asserted, for years, that marriage without children is a form of selfishness whereas, if we consider the welfare of the children, such a marriage may well be an expression of altruism.

And in seeking an answer to the question at the beginning of this chapter: "What right have you to have a child?" although the primary responsibility would seem to be toward the child itself, vastly more is involved, beginning with 2.9 billion other people. How will the birth of another child affect them?

Does the world need more babies at the present time?

Does the United States?

Does any particular family?

Will the world, the United States, and any particular family, be in a better state after the birth of that last child than it was before?

In view of the fact that the birth of every child impinges on the quality of life of other human beings, is the birth of that child going to contribute enough of value to offset the disadvantages its birth (along with millions of others) may result in?

To many readers such questions will seem far-fetched, yet most intelligent people would accept the responsibility of every one of us, not only toward the welfare of his fellow man but also toward the total physical world in which we live, as a cornerstone of an ethical code. It may be more and more difficult, as man's numbers run into the billions, to feel ourselves part of "mankind," and that we are "keepers" of 2.9 billion brothers. But, unless we accept a "right is might" phi-

losophy, we can scarcely justify actions on our part that will
have deleterious effects on our fellow passengers on this
crowded globe. And whether we like to face up to it, or
not, our having children—or not having them—is sure to have
an impact on the lives of our fellow voyagers. When we are
having a hundred million every year, the impact is substantial.

Complete and categorical answers to such questions are extremely difficult because they involve varying human values.
Orthodox Hindus, for example, would presumably welcome as many children as can be born, since it is only through
triumph over trial in numerous reincarnations that the spirit
may eventually find release in Nirvana. There is an interesting ecological problem here: since the number of human
bodies has increased some fifteen times since the days of
Gautama, and the number of "lesser" animals has probably
dropped substantially, the soul's opportunity for a higher
living standard has grown, if only by a redistribution of its
housing, and the centuries of transmigration have presumably
been shortened.

To be consistent, Hindus should probably welcome foreign aid from the United States or technical assistance from
the United Nations, since raising living standards at the human stage would reduce infant mortality and make possible
the conscious self-discipline that promotes the achievement
of bliss for millions of people. Since Hindus make up some
60 per cent of the population of India, their beliefs should
presumably be taken into account in developing our foreign
policy and our Aid-to-India programs.

Thirty years ago militarists would have answered questions
about having children in the affirmative; the Germans, Japanese
and Italians were so short of *Lebensraum*, they demanded larger
populations so they could take somebody else's *Lebensraum*;
cannon fodder is an old excuse for encouraging reproduction.
Whether Mao Tse-tung, who has been acting like a militarist,

also would give such an answer is not entirely clear. Certainly as it applies to military affairs, Mao depends for most of the weapons and equipment that give his armies any effectiveness at all on the relatively less populated U.S.S.R. which, by limiting its population growth, has been able to accumulate capital and raise its standard of living to the point where it can provide Mao what he could not possibly produce at home. In a war between the technologically advanced countries, underpopulated perhaps in Mao's terms, and the more than half billion Chinese, there is no question as to whose technology would win.

Certain employers of cheap labor, such as New York hotel and garment industry men, will join the militarists in approving a higher birth rate. Southerners in the United States have also reported opposition to birth control because it might tend to reduce the supply of cheap Negro labor.

There are the Hutterites and a few other religious sects (*not* necessarily including Roman Catholics) who feel that it is wrong to tamper with God's birth rates, though God's death rates are somehow exempt from the laws of sanctity. Indeed, death rates may even be revised upward, as was pointed out by Dr. L. Harrison Matthews at the British Association for the Advancement of Science, with weapons blessed by opponents of birth control. "Many religious bodies strongly disapprove," he said, "although they condone wars; it is surprising that there are bishops willing to bless battleships, bomber aeroplanes or troops before battle, but who condemn birth control." [11]

There are other religious groups, as in the Netherlands, some rabid nationalists, and ethnic minorities, who feel they can achieve dominance by outbreeding their neighbors. Altogether, however, the pro-natalist group is not very numerous, though it does intimidate politicians and bureaucrats within both the U. S. Government and the United Nations.

It would generally be agreed, except by members of the rather small groups just discussed, that the world as a whole certainly needs no more people.

There are some relatively small areas such as Paraguay, Ecuador and parts of Brazil that could accommodate larger populations if they wanted to turn their society into the kind of world that exists elsewhere. A high material living standard, division of labor, and even diversity of interests and satisfactions, from art and music to science, are not possible if the population is below a certain number. (This need not be large as Norway and Denmark have demonstrated.) On the other hand, when numbers move above a certain maximum in relation to the environment, many satisfactions are lost, some never to be regained.

We should be concerned with what happens at and above these upper levels—and also with what happens on the way to them. The development of Brazil has produced some of the most revolting slums in the history of the world; and the drop in India's death rate, sending the demand for food skyrocketing beyond probability of satisfaction, is bringing that country's zero hour dangerously nearer.

A good deal of serious and responsible thinking on optimum populations, and how to get down to them or up to them, is one of the great needs of our day. Without such consideration it is difficult for the individual to see himself in relation to the society of which he is a member and of the world as a whole, and thus to determine whether or not he has any ethical justification for adding to the population.

The question can be asked in another way, and a simpler answer can be found: if I have another child, will it be at the expense of somebody else?

Shall I be, in effect, a parasite on my friends and neighbors or on other human beings? Have I any right to make demands for which I can give no just recompense? Will the enlargement of my family contribute enough to the future happiness and well-being of other individuals in the world to justify my depriving them of things they want or very much need?

The family on relief, it would seem obvious, should not have more children, since it is already a community burden. Where it does, it is depriving some other family or individual of both the fruits of its labor and the advantages they might bring—better housing, education, books, travel, medical care, security for old age, almost anything one might need or want.

The same statement might be made about the family with three, four or five children "supported" by the father, but which is subsidized by schooling paid for by others, by exemption from income tax payments, by living in a house the mortgage on which is paid by others, etc. In a country plagued by overcrowded schools, overstrained water and sewerage systems and growing scarcity of resources, it is not easy to understand why we should maintain a policy of taxation that encourages population growth in the groups least able to pay for rearing their children.

Indeed, in view of our situation in the world it is doubtful whether we should have governmental policies that encourage any kind of population growth. As was pointed out by the Paley Commission, created by President Truman, we have become a resources-poor, have-not nation. Our high material living standard would collapse if we could not secure raw materials—in mose cases from unrenewable resources from other countries. Most of these countries are growing rapidly and many of them are industrializing. They are going to need their resources at home. In some cases, such as Mexico and Central America, where North American capital has been denuding and eroding once-forested hillsides, they already need the resources. Yet we foreigners are exploiting them to sustain our wasteful standard of living for a rapidly growing population.

This problem is not limited to the New World. At the

United Nations Conference of the Conservation of Natural
Resources which was held in 1949, Italian technicians complained that they knew how to control floods but were not
given a chance. Their attempts to reforest watersheds were
frustrated—of course by the pressure of the Italian population.
They could not "afford" to put land under flood-controlling
trees; it was needed for food-producing crops.

Do we "rich" North Americans have the right to increase
our own population, and thus our drain on raw materials at
the present or future expense of other peoples? Because of the
probable repercussions when these countries recognize that
they have long been victims of a sort of economic colonial-
ism, the maintenance of this drain makes no political sense.
How shall we justify a few hundred millions of dollars in
"aid" when we are bleeding the recipients of the stuff they
will need for their very existence in fifty years?

Since we "pay" for what we get, some of us may reject
the notion that we are considered parasites. But words need
to be given time dimensions and what we pay in 1960 may
have little relevance (to Bolivia's tin, let us say) in the year
1999. We buy certain raw materials from India. This is going
to leave India without these raw materials in 1999, when its
population may have increased 100 per cent, unless there have
been famines. Will not India need these raw materials herself? Even should she not have exhausted her stores, she will
be much worse off *per capita* merely through the growth of
her own numbers, to which we are inexorably contributing
through technical assistance, health, and other programs.

Does the wealthy American family have a right to large
numbers of children, simply because it is rich, because it can
take care of them? The rich, as well as the poor, use water.
They pollute our rivers and our air. They fill up space. They
probably occupy more square yards of road *per capita* than
less prosperous individuals, since they tend to use larger cars.

And they are heavier consumers of resources, especially scarce resources.

A high-minded comment, pertinent here, was made at the World Population Conference held under U.N. auspices in Rome in 1954. The Reverend Stanislas de Lestapis, S.J., in discussing family size, said: "Testimony especially worthy of being imitated is given by the spouses who not only take into consideration their personal welfare—health, physical and psychic energy—but also the welfare of their children, provision for their best possible education, the welfare of the familial community and the nature of its laws of unity and order in intimacy; *and finally, the general welfare of the human community, present and future,* by beginning with the nearest person at the present time."

When occupancy and use of the earth are measured only in money terms, the answers are likely to be highly misleading. This, as has been suggested, is one of the reasons we are in worsening trouble. We are finite, physical beings existing through time; and to disregard our physical needs and their impact on the earth is as blind as ignoring our span of years. "Take no thought for the morrow," has a strange anachronistic sound today.

Of all people who would find it hardest to justify imposing another child on world society, the most conspicuous are those in the underdeveloped countries where plummeting death rates are bringing about explosive population growth. They cannot take care of their own. They are increasingly —like the irresponsibles in our domestic society—expecting to be supported by somebody else.

They want large sums of capital without paying for it or by paying merely nominal sums. They will and often can give no guarantee that it will not be confiscated as were the oil companies in Mexico and Iran, sugar lands in Cuba, and the tin companies in Bolivia. Indeed, expropriation overhangs much foreign investment like a shaky avalanche on a warm spring day.

What the politicians in these countries apparently do not realize is that the money they secure through government loans and grants is not merely pieces of paper or gold; it is working hours, better education, bread and butter, and long-range security taken away from working taxpayers in the granting country.

If it is private investment, it again, represents hard work, self-deprivation, and risk on the part of individual workers. It may be their way of trying to finance education for their children, savings for an old age in which, despite the preposterous label, there is no adequate provision for security.

Yet the countries seeking financial assistance are with very few exceptions, such as India, doing nothing to reduce their birth rates, and, thus, the need to depend on someone else. As is pointed out elsewhere, every child born and living long enough to enter the labor market will require hundreds of dollars (or their local equivalents) in services and equipment merely to provide the facilities for working. In the Caribbean, this has been costing in the neighborhood of $12,000 per job per man; multiply this by a population growth of fifty million a year . . .

While the underdeveloped countries do not even try to stabilize their populations, should they expect someone else to finance their reproduction?

Some dozen years ago, when I suggested that foreign aid be limited to countries whose self-help included birth control, the attacks on me were vitriolic at home and abroad. I was accused of racism and fascism. In the succeeding years our technical aid has been largely responsible for speeding up population growth from 55,000 a day to some 140,000. There are probably five hundred million more people competing for the limited supplies of food than there were in 1948. Many of them would not have to be fed today, had it not been for various American and western European activities.

It is said that a Chinese will not save the life of another since by that act he becomes responsible for the man he saved. Are we not largely responsible to the hungry half-billion? Must we not, in all conscience, feel an obligation to ameliorate their lot? But are we going to continue to build up their numbers to the point where, like hordes of lemmings, they will dash themselves to destruction?

Have they a right to such unrestrained parenthood?

Have we Americans that right in an overpopulated world?

What right has anyone today to have a child if that child is going to swell the world population? Should not all families limit their children at least to the number needed to replace themselves?

This may be the most important question that could be asked in the twentieth century.

8

Success Story

THIS CHAPTER, CONCERNED WITH NORWAY, DENMARK and Sweden, may read something like a love letter and that is what it is meant to be. More than a year in Scandinavia, with literally thousands of miles of travel from Skibotn and Karesuando, in the north, to Møen and Tønders, in the south, has made it possible to visit virtually every province or county in all three countries. Their generous friendliness, their almost unfailing courtesy (the only exceptions were some streetcar crowds in Oslo and a customs officer in Stockholm) and their hospitality toward an American who might just happen to know a relative in "the States," made it possible to become acquainted with all sorts and conditions of men, from cabinet ministers and professors (whose titles have a status far above that of men in similar posts in the United

States) to workers and peasants. Each return to any of the three countries has heightened my regard for them.

A bit of my heart has always been left behind in a number of countries after visits ranging from a few weeks to three years. People vary widely from nation to nation and certainly from observer to observer, but certain admirable traits have seemed especially striking and germane: in Peru, it is the gentleness of the people; in Britain, politically the most civilized country in the world, vigorous and delightful individuality; among the great masses of India the great dignity and self-respect that somehow lifts the individual above the swarming hive in which he has to live; in Japan, the usual if not invariable disciplined courtesy, almost courtliness, of a people forced to develop a *modus vivendi* in a sardine box; in Mexico, the you-be-damned-sir independence that seems to be a blend of Spanish *hidalgoism* and Aztec vigor. Americans have their own engaging—and disenchanting—regional characteristics.

The Scandinavians of the three countries named are not only admirable and likable people; in the ecological sense they are among the most successful, perhaps the most successful, in existence. They have adapted themselves to a harsh and parsimonious environment and by a combination of intelligence, hard work, discipline and what might be called social respect, have achieved one of the truly high living standards. Though both Denmark and Norway proved highly indigestible to the Germans during World War II, as small countries they could scarcely defend themselves indefinitely against rich, strong and powerful invaders from outside; but aside from this danger they would seem to have one of the highest probabilities of future happiness and wellbeing of any country in the world. They arrived at this relatively happy and secure situation by avoiding many of the mistakes that have been made in other parts of the world and by social, technical, artistic and scientific accomplishments that are almost without parallel for countries of their size and relative poverty. It is no accident that the United Nations have found their two staff leaders in Norway and Sweden.

I was fortunate in having one of the most meaningful possible introductions to the northern countries, in 1950, on the seventeenth of May, Norway's national holiday. This is celebrated, not solely with firecrackers and skyrockets, with veterans' and politicians' platitudes, but chiefly with children's parades, the largest in the country's capital. I stood in front of the Royal Palace and, looking down into the heart of the city, watched ranks upon ranks of children marching through the center of the town. Despite the fact that war and occupation lay only five years behind them, they were obviously bursting with health and ready for an all-day hike or ski trip.

Fifteen or twenty abreast, dressed in gay colors, they marched up the hill to the palace where stood the aged King —then well up in his seventies—waiting to receive their salute. The procession passed for hours and neither he nor the youngest parader, who could not have been over six or seven, gave any evidence of fatigue. Among all the thousands there was scarcely a child who did not look as though he combined a sturdy inheritance with an abundance of food, undoubtedly supplemented with cod-liver oil.

I was especially sensitive to the impression given by the singing, cheering youngsters, for my travels during the previous ten years had taken me through country after country where the vigorous-looking child was almost the exception and certainly not the rule. Great brown eyes looking out of sallow, drawn faces; bulging bellies and the apathy that comes from inadequate food and little physical reserve— these were my most vivid memories of children from Mexico to Chile. In Venezuela, then the most prosperous Latin American country because of its great oil sales, the International Labor Organization reported there were some one hundred thousand abandoned children. In one Central American capital, the Health Minister told me, 70 per cent of the children born were illegitimate. One need only look at pictures or watch movies of crowds in Africa, much of Asia, from Italy and Spain, to know that a tragic fate drags down the children of much of the rest of the world. Their lot can be reduced to cold statistics—the number of children per thousand population dying at less than one year of age. The three Scandinavian countries stand near the very bottom of this list. The United Nations Children's Fund has no work to do in Scandinavia.

These children may look forward to a longer life than almost any others in the world; their life expectancy is several years more than those of children in the United States. This life expectancy has increased in Sweden from fifty years to seventy-six since 1900. In Norway it is nearly, if not quite, the longest in the world.

The Scandinavians are among the best-fed people in the world. They not only have sufficient calories and an abundance of proteins and of vitamins; Denmark and parts of Sweden have developed eating to the fine art it is in France.

The high living standards of Scandinavia have been achieved without wrecking the countryside, as has been done in so many other parts of the world, including the United States. The transition from virgin land to desert in little more than a generation is not uncommon in Latin America and is reported to be even more rapid in much of Africa. In Norway, many farms have been in the same family for five or six hundred years and are in better condition today than when the land was first cleared. This throws into dismal relief the millions of acres of American land that have been wrecked by bad farming practices in the century and a half since they were settled.

These statements about Scandinavia are merely headlines and indicators. To understand what these people have accomplished—against the background of misery and threatened catastrophe that spreads across so much of the world—is well worth a closer look.

The northern tip of Norway, the North Cape, is in ap-

proximately the same latitude as the northern tip of Alaska,
Point Barrow, and the 60-degree latitude slightly north of
Oslo almost exactly bisects Hudson Bay; it is far north of the
Aleutian Islands. (Svalbard or Spitzbergen, Norway's nat-
ional source of coal, lies hundreds of miles still farther north,
nearly parallel with the north tip of Greenland.)

It is probable that the first settlers in Norway arrived before the end of the last Ice Age. The full spate of human migration did not come, however, until the ice had moved far
north. These pioneers were probably following the reindeer.
The reindeer today is still a wanderer and one might say
that rather than being domesticated by man, its migratory
habits have forced man to remain a nomad. This was undoubtedly true in ancient times and the first little groups of
hunters drifted back and forth with the seasons, as some of
our Indians did as they followed the bison. The country must
have been largely tundra, occupied along with the reindeer,
by the hare and undoubtedly the lemming hosts and the white
owl that fed upon them.

The earliest human populations in Denmark were there
about ten thousand years ago.[1] In one of the fluctuations that
are so well known for the region, the climate became warmer
and dry. Hunters and fishermen wandering through pine
forests found a great abundance of fish in the streams and
the glacial lakes.

Three thousand years later the climate had become warm
and more humid, and as a consequence oak and beech began
to appear among the conifers. Immigrants continued to press
up from the South and with their domesticated dogs hunted
the aurochs, bear and deer. They were still wanderers and
gatherers, rather than cultivators of food. In their feasting
places they laid down the first kitchen middens to be discovered, deep piles of offal that consist mostly of mussel and
oyster shells.

Perhaps two thousand years later, or some five thousand

years ago, man began to farm the Danish earth. Pigs, cattle and sheep appeared, along with wheat and barley. The Danes have been tilling these soils ever since.

The early invaders of the Norwegian coast, in the small boats that presaged one of the world's great maritime nations, were able to travel north under the beneficent influence of the North Atlantic drift, or extension of the Gulf Stream, which still ameliorates the climate of much of the region. By raising the temperature of the adjacent air and seas, it makes habitable latitudes that in North America and Asia can support only tundra and such animals as caribou, lemmings and foxes with their dependent Eskimos. It is one of the world's greatest air-conditioning units. These first people lived in caves and had only bone and stone implements.

The natural wealth of the sea and land was so great that one wonders whether, if it had been preserved, it might not have been able to support as many people as do the land and sea today. "In the famous Viste archaeological finds on Jaeren, the southwestern coast of Norway, bones of about fifty kinds of animals have been identified, among which only the dog was domesticated. Great schools of whales came to shore, seals were so close in the shallows that the hunter's little boat could hardly make its way between them, and of fish there was an unbounded wealth. Islands were literally covered with sea fowl, providing eggs and down in abundance. The streams teemed with salmon, and in the woods roamed wild animals, both large and small, which could be caught at the drinking and fording places. The big game hunting was often carried on in some spot where reindeer in great herds could be driven out over the steep cliff or precipice and then slain or left to perish . . ." [2] (Scientists are beginning to realize that over large expanses of Africa, as a parallel example, the long-range production of artificial food is not likely to be greater than what can be taken from the native herds of game.)

It was not until the late Stone Age that the interior of Norway began to be occupied. Implements were still crude and ineffectual and these husbandmen, with their cattle, sheep and hogs, settled by such natural meadows as those on which their descendants still cut hay today—perhaps the identical ones. Everywhere along the coast, or by the scores of rivers, boats were nearly as important as cattle, both as a means of travel and as a means of collecting food. The seamanship of which these three nations are so proud today has a tradition as ancient as it is respected.

In the wake of the ice mass, relieved of the pressure of its great weight, the land was rising. Parts of the coast that had long been sea bottom and had accumulated many yards of clay, rose into the air; this movement is still going on so rapidly that Finns are today cultivating areas over which, in their childhood, they passed in boats. Frederikstad Fort, in southern Norway, is supposed to have been under water four hundred years ago. At Lundamo, near Trondheim, terraces deposited under the sea are some five hundred feet above sea level.

During the Bronze Age, which began about 1500 B.C., there was another favorable climate fluctuation and the horse and ox reached Norway. At that time it was not necessary to house the flocks and herds and as a result, there was no collection of manure. Forests were burned to make way for cultivation and soil fertility was quickly exhausted as it is today in most of the Tropics. From this period in Norway there is no trace of permanent farms.

With the dawn of the Iron Age, some twenty-five hundred years ago, there came into being in Scandinavia a cultural pattern that still leaves a very strong mark—the *bondekultur* or peasant society. Iron was abundant in the upper layers of the peat bogs and the ingenious farmers soon learned to dry the peat and build primitive smelters from which they produced material for their tools.

But they were again to suffer a sharp climatic change, near the beginning of the Christian era. They were forced to provide shelter for their cattle and warmer houses for themselves. A more settled agriculture appeared. The *Sandergaard* on Norway's greatest lake, Mjøsa, the oldest known farm settlement, was probably developed about that time. The harsh conditions of the era undoubtedly brought into being an appreciation of the need of co-operation, an attitude that has played a powerful part in these countries ever since. Several families gathered together began to build small settlements and to help one another in the battle against the elements. Until 1940, and the arrival of the Germans, the elements, not man, were the Scandinavian peninsula's chief antagonist. (There were, of course, internal wars.) But they were enemies in only a limited sense: they shaped the character of the people as hands mold clay on a potter's wheel, and helped to build much of the Scandinavian character we know today.

Animal husbandry moved indoors with the climatic change and has been there some two thousand years. In Denmark, with the least severe climate of the three countries, cattle must still be housed seven months out of twelve. This requires good barns and makes agriculture expensive. It also gives a clue to the world—including snow, sleet, wind and cold—in which the Scandinavian must live.

It is important in understanding the Scandinavian way of life to set it against the perspective not only of conditions in the United States but also of other parts of the world where man is struggling with some of the same problems with which the Scandinavian must cope. Nowhere in Scandinavia is climate so delightful as it is in the tablelands of Mexico, Venezuela's Andes, on the Riviera, or in South Africa. We get some measure of the Swede if we meet him in his southern provinces and listen to him talk about his climate with the enthusiasm of a pre-smog Los Angeles booster. In reality, the climate of Scania is more nearly analogous to that of southeastern Alaska than to any other in North America.[3]

The Danish climate is influenced not only by the Gulf Stream but also by the fact that Denmark is a low-lying, relatively level country, surrounded by waters that not only ameliorate the effect of the latitude but counteract the influence of continental climatic forces to the south and east. The average temperature for the year approximates that of Minneapolis, or Madison, Wisconsin, but the variations are much less violent with a range of about 29° Fahrenheit, compared with Minneapolis's 59°.

The position of Denmark between open seas and the great land mass is largely responsible for the buffeting winds that have shaped a great deal of the pattern of the Danish countryside. These winds come, one Danish farmer said to me, "straight from North America." They have forced the Danes to develop the skillfully contrived windbreaks and shelter belts that checkerboard the landscape.

The annual precipitation is about twenty-five inches, comparable to that of London, parts of our Great Plains or the semi-desert state of Bombay in India. Most of the country has some rain from 160 to 180 days a year. Humidity is high, clouds are frequent (tourists in Denmark will find good photographic light rare) and the water that does fall goes farther than in areas marked by high temperatures and clear skies with high evaporation. The fact that the rainfall is less concentrated means that soil erosion is greatly reduced.

Sweden also benefits from the Gulf Stream, though it is greatly influenced on its eastern flank by its junction with the mainland of Eurasia. Its climate is also softened by large inland lakes. It was surprising, on visiting Scania at Thanksgiving time, to find that my host had recently been mowing his lawn.

The mean annual temperature in Sweden ranges from 27° Fahrenheit in the north, or far colder than in any city within the United States, excluding Alaska, to about the temperature of Minneapolis. Winter in the most northern part of Sweden is about 210 days long, from October to April, but in the southernmost counties it runs usually not over 45 days. Snow cover lasts from less than 35 days in the south to more than 250 days in the north. "A good snow cover is of very great importance to the national forestry and agriculture of Sweden as it levels the terrain of the ground, permitting thus easier hauling of the logs to the floatingways; it also protects the winter crops through preventing excessive chilling and freezing of the ground." [4]

Norway's climate, somewhat similar to that of Sweden, is considerably modified along the coast by the fact that the surface is tilted toward the west and the warm seas. Bergen, the chief city of the west coast, has a precipitation of about ninety inches a year, or more than double that of New York and four times that of San Francisco. Farmers near Hamar, which is known to all readers of Sigrid Undset's great Kristen Lavransdatter trilogy, actually resort to irrigation.

Oslo and Burlington, Vermont, have about the same mean annual temperature, although the former city is one thousand miles farther north, whereas Bodø, lying above the Arctic Circle, has a higher mean temperature than Sault Sainte Marie, Michigan. The mean temperatures in January and February in the far northerly cities of Tromsø, Bodø and Vadsø, are all fifteen or more degrees above zero, Fahrenheit! (Parenthetically much of the northern hemisphere has been enjoying a favorable climatic change that may reverse itself, with adverse effects on food production, at any time.)

What much of the Scandinavian landscape looks like is suggested, as a number of people have pointed out, by the parts of the United States to which immigrants from these countries traveled. A large proportion of Swedes settled in Illinois and Minnesota, where they found rolling, fertile plains in many ways reminiscent of the best farm land in their home counties of Scania. The Norwegians—those who did not stop in Brooklyn, as much a focus of shipping as their native Bergen—went largely on to the more wooded country of Minnesota and Wisconsin, where in the forests, with more acid soils than on the prairies, they found an aspect and a climate more nearly like Norway. Many Danes—again those who passed beyond the port of Brooklyn—have scattered over the rolling plains of Illinois, Iowa, Minnesota and Nebraska.

If we include in its area all the offshore skerries and the great Arctic archipelago of Svalbard, Norway has an area a little larger than Montana. (This is approximately the area of Japan with a population of 93,000,000 whereas Norway's is 3,500,000.) The traveler in Norway might be reminded both of Alaska and Chile. It is a rugged, mountainous country, marked by a series of high plateaus and mountains, some of which are covered by glaciers. Most of the precipitous west coast is dissected by fjords and rivers. Off the mouth of the fjords and along much of the coast there is a fringe of hundreds of rocky islands, or skerries, that as in the case of Alaska and Chile provide an inland passage protected against the great storms from the open sea.

From southwestern Norway, along the coast and well down the western flank of Sweden, the landscape is very like that of coastal Maine and the farming-fishing-lumbering pattern of economic development is not dissimilar.

Spectacular gorges, cut inland from the Norwegian fjords, carry roaring torrents down from the high uplands, in rapids and cascades that are being turned into one of Norway's greatest assets, hydroelectric power. Here—at least until the engineers befoul it—one finds a landscape that is equaled in natural beauty by few parts of the world. Only about 3 per cent of Norwegian land is under cultivation, about 25 per cent is in forests. Optimists believe that the agricultural area can be doubled, but most of the remaining 65 to 70 per cent consists largely of the high brushy fells that are decreasingly used for grazing and increasingly for tourists and skiing.

Nature has dealt more gently with the Swedes. About 10 per cent of their land is under the plow and most Swedes suffer from the delusion that they are self-sufficient in food. They overlook, of course, their dependence on imported fertilizers, oil for the mounting number of tractors, and supplementary food imports.

Sweden has been described by some geographers as a "lakescape." She is also a land of many rivers, waterfalls and rapids that provide much hydroelectric power and are far more useful than are most of the Norwegian rivers for moving the all-important timber. These rivers have also been, throughout the centuries, a source of fish, including salmon and salmon trout which are without equal in any other part of the world I have visited for delicacy of flavor. Their existence is, unfortunately, threatened by hydroelectric developments.

Denmark (excluding Greenland) is a tiny country, about twice the size of Massachusetts, and nearly everything in it is on a small scale. Hills are small, forests are small, salmon rivers would be considered mere rills in the United States; and the landscape is divided into miniature farms and, for the most part, small towns. Over the greater part of the country the soil is also poor and that of the large peninsula of Jutland was, before cultivation, little better than quartz sand.

As one would expect in a humid climate, Scandanavian soils are leached and highly acid. This has long made for difficult agriculture. In Norrbotten, in the north of Sweden, an area that occupies nearly one-quarter of the total area of the country, there are only about two hundred thousand acres of arable land with a little more of meadow of varying quality, some nine million of productive woodland and about fifteen million labeled "unproductive." (In terms of cash the "unproductive"

land, one of the world's great tourist attractions, probably
brings in more income than the scattering of small farms.)

Of the three countries Sweden is the only one well endowed with minerals, though Norway has been developing
not inconsiderable iron mines at Mo i Rana, since World War
II.

For centuries the people of the three countries existed in
their harsh environment chiefly by the arduous means of
lumbering and fishing, which even today take many lives, and
Naturhusholdning or subsistence, self-sufficient farming.

There are few better farmers anywhere. The hundreds of
miles of stone walls in Norway and Sweden, comparable to
those of New England, except that in Scandinavia these walls
are often nearly wide enough to carry a jeep, are a monument
to the industry—and the harsh environment—in which these
people not only lived but flourished for centuries. Whereas
on most continents from southern Europe to Africa, the
Americas and Asia, man has abused and often completely
ruined his soil, the Scandinavians have developed a pride in
their land and a devotion to it that imposes on the farmer an
obligation to pass on the farm to his son in better condition
than he received it. Such laws as the *Odelsrett* or entailment
to the eldest son, have avoided the extreme fragmentation of
the land that makes productive agriculture almost impossible in such countries as those of the Middle East and India.
Though the tradition of the small farmer is strong, for decades all three countries have—in the interest of higher living
standards—been consolidating holdings to constitute not big
farms but larger workable areas. This has been made both
feasible and desirable by modern mechanized agriculture.

There were major migrations to the New World in the
nineteenth and early twentieth centuries. As is pointed out
elsewhere, birth rates have been falling for two hundred
years and the need for escape has been at least temporarily
abated.

The contribution that these people have made in the history of civilization is out of all proportion to their numbers, and has certainly not been a function of their wealth. They have developed within the framework of their limited monarchies —which some of them consider to be rather ridiculous and expensive relics—as thoroughgoing democracies as are to be found anywhere in the world. Partly because the populations of the countries are small, they operate like somewhat extended town meetings. It is probable that no part of the world has more honest government than Scandinavia, nor a better informed citizenry. Literacy is all but universal, newspapers have higher standards than all but the best in the United States, and the state radios operating under the direction of citizens' committees put to shame the cheap commercialism that has taken over so much of the American airways. Such corruption as has long plagued Boston, New York, Chicago and other American cities is unknown throughout Scandinavia. Indeed, the behavior of every man in public life is so well known that the rise of a Scandinavian Huey Long, Jim Curley or Jimmy Walker would be inconceivable.

These people have developed democratic co-operation to a degree without equal anywhere in the world. Marquis Childs in *Sweden, The Middle Way* has made co-operation in Sweden world-famous; but though less known, it has been quite as important in Norway and Denmark. Co-operation in Denmark has been particularly significant, both because it stimulated and set the pattern for much of the co-operation in the other two countries and because, in view of the intrinsic poverty of the country resulting from the limited resources available, the results are even more noteworthy than elsewhere.

Danish co-operatives grew out of free associations of individuals in large numbers of voluntary organizations, and acted as a training ground for political democracy. As in the

American colonies, and in the development of the co-operative movement in Britain, the early co-operative associations were developed by civic or national leaders, who were often, themselves, rich men.

Usually one such individual, or a small group of men, would organize a meeting to obtain support for some such venture as a co-operative store. Rule by the democratic majority was general and as Henning Ravnholt points out, "it increased the small holder's confidence to know that his vote at the general meeting was as good as that of the large farmer." [5]

An important influence in the rise of the Danish co-operative movement was the folk high school. Here, through a kind of adult education that is again almost unique in Scandinavia, farmers and workers received an education that, primarily liberal and non-technical, provided them with the adaptability and perspective that they found indispensable as the co-operative movement grew. In the early Danish co-operatives, part of the earnings was put aside for educational work.

An increasing number of folk high schools now teach "co-operation" directly, as a sort of technology, and a Danish co-operative college has been set up at Middelfart. As well as teaching practical operation of co-operatives, it gives instruction in subjects of a more general educational character.

In its down-to-earth functioning the typical consumers' co-operative society reminds one, again, of the New England town meeting. Government is in the hands of the members; they exercise their authority at the general meeting, where decisions affecting the society are made. The general meeting elects an executive committee which controls the daily work of the society and makes decisions on all important matters not referred to the general meeting. It also elects the society's auditors who supervise the financial side of the society's activities. The manager is appointed either by the executive committee or by the general meeting.

These societies, in which the members actually have a voice, are very different to American corporations. These have, especially in recent years, made much of the fact of their shareholders' representing a cross section of the American people. They imply that this results in democratic management. In reality, of course, most stockholders have no effective voice in the management. As long as the number of the shareholder's votes is determined by the amount of stock he owns, concentration of power will almost always remain in the hands of the few individuals. The structure of Danish co-operatives is designed to exclude exactly this situation.

One of the most interesting aspects of Danish co-operatives is the members' joint responsibility for the co-operative's economic liabilities. The fact that, in the first difficult and precarious years of the co-operative movement, simple and poor peasants should have been willing to put everything they possessed into such shaky enterprises as the early co-operative societies showed their genuine faith in the principle of co-operation.

The first successful Danish co-operative store, which was a direct imitation of the Rochdale Society, was opened at Thisted in 1866. One of the founders of this society was Pastor Hans Christian Sonne, who was distressed by the miserable conditions under which workers were obliged to live. He even held meetings in a warehouse for workers who stayed away from Church because they felt they lacked decent clothes. Like the earlier "potato priests," who, from the pulpit, promoted the wide planting of potatoes, Sonne was a practical man. "My audience," he said, "soon gave me to understand that if I wanted to be of help to them, I must first help them to obtain their daily bread."

The growth of the movement, according to *Det Danske Selskab*, from which much of this information is drawn, could almost be measured by the number and viciousness of the attacks upon it. It was alleged that the co-operative stores were illegal gin mills, that they were encouraging drunkenness and licentiousness, and demoralizing the young people of the villages. They were accused of charging high prices for sugar that was 25 per cent sand!

A variety of devices was used in attempts to scuttle the co-operative movement. For example, in 1900, a combine of tobacco manufacturers adopted the policy of refusing the ordinary wholesale discount to the co-operative stores. The wholesale society countered by buying a tobacco factory at Esbjerg, and brought the manufacturers to heel.

The price policy of the co-operative societies has usually been to charge the going price at the stores and return profits to the members in the form of a dividend at the end of the year. The Danish wholesale society has branches for a variety of articles including groceries, clothing, books, shoes, hardware and seed, and factories producing exclusively for the retail societies with the help of technical departments, such as an experimental laboratory, engineering and architectural departments, publicity, accounting, auditing, etc. The co-operative publication "Samvirke" is said to have the largest circulation of any newspaper in Denmark.

In 1941, a book-publishing association was set up, financed by other co-operative societies. With "Samvirke" as an available advertising medium it has been an effective way of getting good and cheap books sold throughout the country. Publishing in the Scandinavian countries is, by American standards, almost incredibly successful. Despite the small populations and limited markets, publishers carry large lists and print beautiful books, such as practically no American publisher would touch because they would be too expensive.

Agricultural co-operatives have been especially important

in Denmark where nearly half the farmers possess less than twenty-five acres; the co-operatives have brought to these small farmers many of the advantages that in most parts of the world are available only to large and wealthy agriculturists.

One of the most famous men in the history of Denmark was E. M. Dalgas. He was a mechanical engineer whose road-building activities had made him familiar with most parts of his country. When, after 1864, Denmark had lost not only the war with Prussia but the provinces of Schleswig-Holstein, Dalgas popularized the motto: "What we have lost without, we must win within." He founded the *Danske Hedeselskab* for the reclaiming of the great Jutland plain. This is an area formerly wooded, now normally dominated by heather (whence the name of the Heath Society) which is itself usually an indicator of poor soils.

Dalgas went to work with characteristic Danish ingenuity and vigor and well over a million acres of the extremely poor heath soil has now been reclaimed. Production here is lower than on the superior soils of Zealand, but by a combination of manuring, marling, in recent years the use of artificial fertilizers, and drainage, yields have been going up. A farmer of the Jutland heath who, by Paul Bunyanesque efforts, is turning wasteland into a farm of high productivity, said to me with a twinkle in his eye, "You see, we do not have to go to America. There is still plenty to be done here at home."

Out of the co-operatives grew, in 1900, a "butter-brand association" made up of dairies that had agreed to meet certain standards. The Bronze Age trumpet, or *lur*, was adopted to mark the brand. This was so successful that in 1906 the *lur* was made compulsory by law as the brand of all Danish butter and cream exported and all export products were required to meet the high standards of the butter-brand association.

In 1911, at the instigation of the dairies, a law was passed making the use of the *lur* conditional on high standards of water contents, pasteurization and taste. Since these laws accomplished the purposes of the brand association, it was dissolved in 1915.

Very much the same reform took place with respect to Danish bacon. The English market, which was buying most of the products of the pig farms, demanded a lean meat and the pig breeders rapidly streamlined their sides of bacon; it has little resemblance to the chunks of fat that are sold as bacon in the United States. (It is, readers may be interested to know, exported in tins and sold here at little more than the price of the strips of American fat.) American butchers, to conceal the character of their product, have of course taken to packing it with a thin overlap, so that the purchaser can get no idea of what he is buying until he opens the package at home. The Danish farmer tries to gives the customer what he wants.

There is a bewildering range of products and functions of co-operatives: co-operative egg-export associations; poultry-killing stations; co-operatives for domestic and foreign marketing of cattle; a seed co-operative that exports to countries as distant as Argentina; co-operative fertilizer and fodder societies; a co-operative cement factory and bank, as well as a large group of village banks; a co-operative insurance company, etc. Rocky mountain trout is bred in Denmark, frozen, and shipped as far as California.

The first co-operative consumers' societies in Norway were founded in 1851 under the leadership of Marcus Thrane, a labor leader and the son of a parson, who was actually imprisoned because of his activities! It is said that the development was indigenous, without any inspiration from the English Rochdale movement. The early attempts failed, but a few years later the authorities withdrew some of their opposition. In 1875 there were 276 co-operative consumers' societies, with over thirty thousand members. This has grown to well over

1,000 such societies, two bakeries and more than fifty purchasing co-operatives, with over a quarter of a million members. It was estimated a few years ago that more than 30 per cent of the Norwegian population buys its staples through consumers' co-operatives.

An endowed foundation called *Selskapet for Norges Vel* or Association for Norwegian Welfare, was established early in the nineteenth century. For its time it was a unique organization and now, as the Royal Norwegian Agricultural Society, its orientation is clearly defined.

In 1830 the Society began to organize local agricultural groups, *Landbruksselskaper,* and today there is one in every Norwegian county. These societies, like the Danish Agricultural Council, employ technicians who function much as do extension agents in the United States. The *Selskap for Norges Vel* has been a powerful promoter and supporter of co-operation. Co-operative dairies have been organized from one end of the country to the other and they now have a virtual monopoly of the milk business. They have promoted an equalization of prices but, with typical Norwegian reasonableness, have kept these from becoming exorbitant.

In the smaller cities dairies usually have their own outlet shops but in larger towns much of the milk is sold, in pleasant little neighborhood stores, by private shopkeepers. Since these are not members of the co-operative organization they receive what amounts to merely a nominal remuneration and handle the milk not for profit but because it brings people into their stores.

An interesting aspect of the dairy co-operative organization is that the shares in the co-operative belong not to the farmer but to the farm and if this changes hands, the shares go with it.

Here, in the United States, agriculture in many areas is in a parlous condition because the prices received by the farmers have not risen nearly as high nor as rapidly as the prices they pay. (It is often difficult not to suspect that the cost of their overhead is inflated and that they are, frequently, really living beyond their means.) Ever since the beginning of World War II the prices paid by the consumer have risen, in part to cover the costs of "servicing," such as fancy packages designed to sell more food, and partly because the food is now sold in a semiprocessed condition, canned, frozen or dried. Some of the overload of cost is undoubtedly justified, but an enormous cut goes to the middleman without benefit either to the consumer or the producer. This, the Scandinavians, especially the Norwegians, have largely avoided through their co-operative organizations. As one watches the functioning of the co-operatives it is difficult not to conclude that they are invaluable both to the farmers and to the city folk. Yet for some reason they have caught on in only a limited way in the United States. They might well be a partial answer to inflation and the high cost of living that is often the result of debasing the quality of the product, and bilking the public. It may be that the smallness of Scandinavian countries, with their resultant improved communications, helps them to do what we Americans have not been able to achieve.

Co-operation in Scandinavia has grown naturally out of social institutions that go far back into the Middle Ages. One of the most interesting of these is the *Almenning* or community forest. This is of double interest because out of it came the habit of using and managing the land and its resources in a co-operative community; and because, hundreds of years ago, it set the pattern for almost universal forest management, such as the United States, for example, has achieved chiefly on government land and such private lands as belong to major lumber companies. (Japanese and European visitors to this country express their horror at the wasteful, destructive forest practices that characterize most of the hundreds of millions of acres of forest land privately owned in small parcels.)

The forest situation in Scandinavia is not ideal, as I shall explain later; but there is much that we—who are a very long way from resolving our forest problems—could learn, both from the history of the old community forests in Norway[6] and some of the most advanced modern forest management to be found anywhere in the world.[7]

Agricultural land has suffered little from intensive cultivation over hundreds of years; indeed, in most places from Finnmark to Jutland it has been improved. There is hardly a suggestion of the vast areas seriously damaged or destroyed, with which we are familiar in North and South America, Africa, Southern Europe, Asia, Australia and New Zealand.

The Scandinavian farmer has been aided in his conservation practices by the gentle North European rainfall pattern, but even more by his attitude toward the land. Most of the farmers of Norway, Sweden and Denmark would no more regard their land as simply the means of a livelihood than they would put a sister out to prostitution. Agriculture in these three countries is truly a way of life and "economic man" has as yet not made enough inroads on the *bondekultur* to have become a threat to the fertility and stability of the land itself. Here, after hundreds of years of intense cultivation, were found some of the highest yields per acre, and before the development of modern fertilizers. There may be some danger in the fact that the empirical peasant skills that so long maintained the productivity of the land are being replaced by modern technology that is still only partially understood. For example, manuring is giving way to chemical fertilizing. What effect the new fertilizers may be having on the structure of the soil so carefully, indeed so lovingly, maintained and improved over generations by careful cultivation, is not clear. Neither does there seem to be much concern with the effect of monocultures—pine after pine, spruce after spruce—on forest soils. In a year of travel in Scandinavia I was able to find only one individual who was even concerned with this problem. He was a Swedish microbiologist who summed up his attitude in the one sentence: "The more we care for our forests, the sicker they get."

This is not to imply a lack of research by Scandinavian foresters and agriculturists. Norway, Denmark and Sweden have long been leaders in these fields. Swedish genetic investigations are famous and in their tree-breeding programs they are years ahead of the United States. While we have been cutting our finest trees, they have been saving them as a source of seed. However, technology and economics seem to have overrun science to some extent and the short range, empirical "profit-taking" view is prevailing.

The three countries are, of course, famous for their welfare developments.

If we tend to take such programs more or less for granted we should recall the abandoned children in Venezuela, already mentioned; and the similar phenomenon, though on a smaller scale, in Bogotá, Colombia, where, in the mid-Forties it was no unusual thing to see five- and six-year-olds scrummaging in garbage cans under the cold rain. And these are far from being poor, backward countries.

So famous are the welfare developments in Sweden, and so interesting to Americans, that we have become a good deal of a nuisance. A few years ago it was even necessary to have special government personnel in welfare departments assigned to take care of foreigners, primarily from the United States.

No one is hungry in Scandinavia (which can scarcely be said for our West Virginia coal fields and our Indian reservations), old age is decently cared for (in contrast to the quasi-charnel houses labeled "nursing homes" that are burgeoning across our rich land), and health care is generally of a high order, though perhaps not the equal of the best in the United States.

Housing has, for a variety of reasons, lagged behind other developments. An official report published in 1953 says: "Practically all urban dwellings in the Northern countries today have electricity and water closets; in Denmark, Iceland, Norway and Sweden, one-third or more have a bathroom: central heating has been widely introduced, particularly in Sweden." [8]

(As I traveled from one end of Sweden to the other in 1950 I was impressed by the number of hotels that had ballrooms but no baths. "It wasn't so bad," as the headwaiter in Skellefteå commiserated, "before they closed the public baths.") Housing shortcomings have had a powerful influence on the behavior and well-being of the people. Small apartments, for example, have done far more to set a small family pattern— to make birth control effective—than all the educational efforts of the health authorities.

It is difficult and in a sense meaningless to get statistics on the reading of books, in part because definitions of what books "are" vary widely, and Mickey Spillane is hardly comparable to Arnold Toynbee. However, for what the information may be worth, the Scandinavians are almost, if not quite, without peers in both the quality and quantity of their reading. Visits to many bookstores, in various parts of the three countries, left at least this observer with the impression that the intellectual level of the books was probably superior to that of any country in the Americas or Western Europe. The personal libraries of even small farmers are often of such a quality that no American school teacher or even college professor would feel ashamed of them.

The reading of good books is, of course, only one evidence of the high cultural level of Scandinavia. With well under 1 per cent of the world's population and a proportion of its wealth that is perhaps not much higher, it has had a major influence on the development of the modern theatre, chiefly through Ibsen; has produced outstanding literature from the Eddas to the novels of Hamsun, Undset, Lagerlöf, Lagerkvist, and Bojer, to name a few; a long line of notable painters, including Edvard Munch; perhaps the greatest wildlife painter in history, Bruno Liljefors, all but unknown outside his native Sweden; music that, if not the greatest, stands high in world repertoires; noteworthy ballet and outstanding architecture and design. The accomplishments of the Scandinavians in physics, oceanography, genetics, biology, etc., are out of all proportion to their populations. Norwegian meteorologists, for example, virtually revolutionized thinking in this field before World War II and during it.

To sum up, Norway, Denmark and Sweden have achieved, measured by almost any norm one could think of, one of the most advanced civilizations in the history of mankind. Not a single country in all of Latin America or Africa even begins to compare with them; and in variety of accomplishments no country in Asia, with the possible exception of Japan, begins even to approach them. While we have outstripped them in some mechanical skills (though our agricultural production per acre is still far below that of Scandinavia) we have certainly not produced a musician comparable to Grieg, a dramatist with the power and influence of Ibsen, and perhaps no novelist or poet the equal of the best of Norway, Denmark and Sweden. When we recall that only a hundred years ago, as we have said, these were poor, underdeveloped, peasant countries, living chiefly by fishing and subsistence farming, their achievements are especially impressive.

In the world today new nations, based largely on subsistence agriculture, with high aspirations toward political and economic progress, are unfolding like leaves in the spring. So it may serve a useful purpose to explore briefly, even if superficially, some of the reasons why the Scandinavian countries have in less than a century, developed out of an obscurity that—except for their quondam war-like pro-clivities—left them unknown, to a status that is universally admired.

This is, of course, a subjective appraisal on my part. Among themselves the Scandinavians do not agree either on their present status nor as to explanations as to how they got that way, in spite of a good deal of soul-searching over the years. At the present time Sweden, the most "Americanized" of the three countries, is rather looked down upon by many Nor-wegians as "decadent." The young people especially tend to scorn the Swedes for spending their afternoons in motion-picture theatres instead of climbing mountains, hiking or ski-ing! Some Swedes, with a higher monetary and material living standard, frequently regard the Norwegians and Danes as rather uncouth peasants. Many Danes, who are among the gayest people in the world, shake their head over the dourness of their northern neighbors! And they say, "When they want to have a good time, they must come to Denmark."

It is indubitably true that Danish beer has a higher alcoholic content than Swedish and that the Swede getting off the ferry boat in Malmö is a merrier man than he would be in his own country.

To "explain" Scandinavia would not be easy and it would certainly be presumptuous unless one had spent many years studying the various countries. In view of the way they have lifted themselves by their own bootstraps and of what so much of the rest of the world might learn from them, they would seem somewhat more worthy of study than primitive tribes. Yet no one has produced a book on any of the coun-tries comparable to de Tocqueville or Lord Bryce on Amer-ica. The really good, over-all book has not yet been written on Norway, Sweden or Denmark.

Some phenomena and influences would seem, however, without question to have had a powerful influence in molding the character of these people, their social organization, and their way of life.

The topography of their lands has certainly had a strong impact upon them that is now to some extent weakening. It is said of Norway that she is "divided by land and united by sea." Rocky, desert-like plateaus, high mountains, deep fjords, and rushing rivers for centuries tended to isolate groups of Norwegians from one another. When long winters are added to the physical barriers, the need for co-operation, and at the same time a healthy self-reliance, must have followed naturally. Of the three peoples, the Norwegian seems to have developed most individuality, and, at the same time, a streak of romanticism that peoples the country's stark hills and deep forests with trolls and other wayward spirits. The wild and magnificent beauty of Norway is also, probably, reflected in the great development of Norwegian painting and sculpture which finds an impressive, if somewhat bewildering, culmination in Oslo's Vigeland Park.

The harsh land developed a steady, frugal, farsighted and hard-working people. If you did not get your wood in, in the fall, you did not repeat the mistake. You did not have a chance to.

A famous Swedish essay by Carl J. L. Almqvist, *The Meaning of Swedish Poverty*, published in the early nineteenth century, combines a vigorous nationalism with a Spartan admonition not only to triumph over the lean environment, but to revel in the conquest. "If you are born in Sweden and still have a young and plastic mind," he writes, "then you should go out among the people and above all not despise anybody or anything. Look at the pale green leaves on our trees; they are not juicy and dark green as in the South—our love in this country does not come from desire but . . . from poverty, solitude and need, and sometimes, perhaps, from soul and heaven. It is difficult to explain why, but that is the way it is. Teach yourself to bear the misfortunes typical of this country;

they may hurt your body or your clothes, but will not injure the depths of your heart. Understand what it is to get along without things. When you get along without, and endure, be glad to do it. If you show any bitterness over misfortunes, you have still something foreign in your blood. . . .

"There is one thing the Swede is made for, unlike the rest of Europe, and that is poverty. If we could only learn that! All of us share it, more or less, here, but many do not behave as they should with the lot God has given us. The Swede is poor. If he understands that, he has grasped the core of his nationality and is then undefeatable.

"To be poor means to be thrown upon one's own resources.

"Poverty is not something to strive after, not a goal toward which one should work. But the man who is poor is dependent only on himself. Not to perish but to survive, to develop from oneself what one needs, that is to be poor. To understand this in the right way, with freedom and independence, is to find within oneself an inexhaustible resource for help, and there also to find skill, alertness and good thinking, to help in all situations—this power is the essence of Swedish nationality, such as God and nature have provided us. . . .

"To seek poverty purposely is very different from what is here in question: to be able to make oneself rich if one wants to and at times even to do it. A man who is rich in this way has a large fortune indeed, when he is able to do without things at will, and it is important. He is not dependent upon his treasures; he uses them as he pleases. On the other hand, he who is rich without this kind of fortune is a very weak creature. His well-being and his entire personality lie in his possessions; he lives outside his own person and does not dare the smallest thing for fear of death or destruction. No one is more impregnable than he who is independent of everything except himself. Nobody can rob him of anything he desires. He can take what he wants and leave the rest."

Almqvist rejected self-imposed poverty and the self-sacri-
fice such as were sought by some of the saints in the Middle
Ages. "In Sweden it is beside the point to *seek* for poverty. It
is a dowry from nature: it is not a goal to strive for, but something to start from. To be poor is not a political or religious
pose here; it is the Swede's lot in the world. If he understands
this, then he has the ability to be poor, the strength that will
meet demands made on it. This is what the Swedish farmer
knows better than anything else and what the Swedish ruling
classes must get used to if they want to understand the basis
of Swedish nationalism."

He goes on to say, "Of all European countries none is as
detached and dependent upon itself alone as is our peninsula. All the other countries have more or less a relationship,
both in a literary and political sense. They are like brothers.
Our country is nearly an island and as a result we are geographically isolated. Our inner nature is that of the islander
left to himself. Scandinavia must be self-contained or fall.
It does have various relationships with the rest of Europe,
but these are only nominal and there is little, in reality." [9]

It would be interesting to have Almqvist's judgement on
the 1960 Swede! He has the highest living standard on the
continent of Europe and an economy so integrated with the
rest of the world as to be dependent upon it both for markets
and for supplies, without which even the very process of food
production would fail! There is little doubt that the poverty
exalted by Almqvist, and the need to "make do," molded the
character of Scandinavians in a way that has begun to break
down only within the last few decades. Hard work, co-operation, honesty, the maximum use of one's intelligence, social and
personal discipline, are all characteristics fostered by the hard
life on the poor and often isolated farms. If a tool broke, a man
repaired or remade it himself. Some of the most interesting
and ingenious simple farm implements to be found anywhere
in the world can be seen in the agricultural museums of the

three countries. (Compare these with the digging stick that so long served the Indian peasants in Central America, and the wooden plow on which the Indian in Asia still depends.) Out of isolation developed the charming peasant folk art of Norway and Sweden that was later to influence the painting, sculpture, architecture and design that are famous throughout the western world.

The psyche in which rich, organic individual responsibility developed its permanent structure, as the farmer built the structure of his soil, was ready for the Reformation, and it is difficult not to conclude that Protestantism (or at least the escape from Roman Catholicism) was a major force in Scandinavian progress. As one looks at the so-called Christian nations today, it is significant that those more than nominally Catholic are the ones most lacking in the achievements that we consider mark a high standard of living: Poland, Portugal, Italy, Spain, Ireland, most of Latin America, and even Catholic sections of non-Catholic countries, such as Bavaria and French Canada. These are about as far from Scandinavia, in terms of social and economic welfare, as one could imagine.

Pragmatism and the growth of the scientific spirit in Scandinavia have not only guided the way of life (though largely within the frame of Christian ethics) but have made most human progress possible.

At least two hundred years ago the Scandinavian people (not their governments) began to develop such a rational population policy and system of birth control as the Roman Catholic Church keeps much of the world from achieving today. (See page 211.) Without birth control, breeding at the leporine rate of the Roman Catholic countries, Scandinavia would probably be as badly off as El Salvador.

Scandinavia has known overpopulation in the past, but unlike many other countries it has learned from experience. The *Gota Saga*, written about 1350, recalls that from the first three denizens of the local Garden of Eden, "the number of

inhabitants increased so rapidly for a long time that the
country was not able to feed them all. Then it was decided by
lot that every third person should leave the land, but that
those exiled should be allowed to keep and carry away all that
they owned above ground." [10] The emigrations to America
in the nineteenth century were in part motivated by population pressures at home, but birth rates have continued to fall
and the population of the three countries has been growing
very slowly.

There is a direct line of evolution from the Reformation,
through translation of the Bible into vulgar language, the
requirement that all ready for confirmation know how to
read the Bible, and Bishop Grundtvig's founding and promo-
tion of the folk high schools, to the spirit of free inquiry,
recognition of realities, and the willingness to act upon them,
as it exists today. The fact that while Mexico was building churches, Norway, Sweden and Denmark were building
schools probably explains more than any other single factor
the wide disparity in their living standards.

The fact that the Industrial Revolution came late to Scandinavia has also contributed to its high living standard.
Large cities are of recent development and before slums
had a chance to spread, the Scandinavians, whose leaders
have in recent years been closely in touch with developments
abroad, began to come to grips with the problems of urbanization. The people moving into the towns have brought with
them patterns of country living, including a respect for one's
home; overcrowded though many of them are, these city
dwellers have maintained such order and decency as one ex-
pects to find in their rural farm houses. The poorest sections
of the cities are not slums, simply because Scandinavians will
not tolerate slums. They have too much respect for themselves
and the way they live. Today, as a rule, they control the size
of their families before they become overcrowded. Paint and
flowers cost little and the poorest blocks of flats never look

like such plague spots as are far too common in Chicago, Detroit, New York, Washington, Rio de Janeiro, Mexico City, Naples, Rome, Paris—or almost any large city in the world.

A most notable characteristic of the Scandinavian has been his love for, and protection of, the natural beauty of his country. When, despite the decades of attempts to instill such understanding in this country, we see some of the most beautiful areas being taken for industry—the banks of the Hudson River, the sand dunes of Indiana—we must both respect and envy the Scanians whose planning law provides that, in general, lakes are to be left fringed with trees.

The restraint and good taste that seem all but universal among these people protect their island summer colonies from such rural slums as are taking over the Atlantic Coast, and making the area between San Francisco and San Diego one long series of hot-dog stands and honky tonks. Some of the most beautiful skiing and hiking country in the world can still be found within ten or fifteen minutes' streetcar ride from the center of Oslo. And here one may commonly see the black cock, one of the largest game birds of Europe. Moose graze not only on the outskirts of Swedish towns but occasionally wander into as highly industrialized and developed areas as Gothenburg. One of the great pleasures to be experienced in Scandinavia, now that Roger Tory Peterson has produced a European guide, is a bird-watching tour from the North Sea to the North Cape. Norwegians, Danes and Swedes bring to their outdoors an intelligent understanding and appreciation, and therefore an enjoyment, such as has hardly begun to grow in the United States. The Scandinavians have a real capacity to think and, what is more, they enjoy it.

These countries have not achieved Utopia. Well-being is a relative state and there are many defects. Sweden is organized and "socialized"—though nominally free enter-

prise actually carries on most of the country's business—to a
degree that is distressing to most foreigners and even to
many Swedes. Individual opportunity is so limited that many
people have a deep sense of frustration. For example, in 1950,
less than 2 per cent of the people in the country had an income of more than $4,000 a year. The "leveling down" proc-
ess that has gone so far in Britain and is making such headway
in America is developing a monotony and limitation of social
mobility that for many people take much of the zest out of
living. And while these countries are not overpopulated in
the sense of Asian and Latin American nations with uncon-
trolled birth rates, they are close enough to the saturation
point so that the individual, although he may have enough
to eat and a roof over his head, finds other satisfactions lacking. Greta Garbo's unaffected, "I vant to be alone," might
almost be a national motto.

Swedish universities are superior, in their graduate departments, to all but the very best in the United States. They
produce outstanding scholars, who then find few opportunities to realize the full capabilities of their intellect and training. Scandinavian school systems are full of frustrated men
and women who, in terms of their careers, have no place to
go.

The extremely high suicide rate that characterizes Denmark and, to some extent Sweden (in general, Protestants who
kill, kill themselves, Catholics each other) seems to find its
most plausible explanation in terms of frustration.

As a brilliant Danish doctor, who had himself treated over
two hundred would-be suicides, put it, "In Denmark there is
so little to look forward to—and so little to worry about.
When a man is twenty-two or twenty-three, he has a pretty
clear idea of what he will be doing at sixty or sixty-five. He
also knows as he approaches sixty or sixty-five that he can
count on a roof over his head and at least adequate food to
eat. There is little chance to improve oneself." The man or

woman who finally resorts to suicide is, undoubtedly, an extremely atypical individual and should not be given too great importance as what ecologists call an "indicator."

An undoubted factor in suicide rates is the rootlessness of many Scandinavians. Though the industrial worker may still, in some cases, maintain contact with the farm home, he is psychologically a displaced person. The close bonds that once supported the family of several generations have been loosened with consequent strains of different kinds on the old and young.

While he still worked on the farm, the peasant was at least reasonably sure that under all except the very worst conditions he could at least have enough fish and potatoes to sustain him and his family. He now depends on the often erratic vagaries of world economic conditions, and if these create unfavorable situations for Scandinavia, the worker is dependent on government handouts of uncertain value.

Instead of dealing in terms of everyday realities, such as soils, cattle, timber, etc., the worker's life is now controlled by many symbols which, especially in this day of managed currencies, are of highly uncertain meaning. A wrong guess by Swedish economists who expected a major postwar depression in the United States led to the reduction of Swedish gold reserves from $482,000,000 at the end of 1945 to $81,000,000 by the middle of 1948.

Under the conditions that obtained until quite recently, the vast preponderance of Scandinavians, living as peasants, were creative workers. Most of them have now been turned into mere machine tenders. Interesting understanding of this was expressed by a Jutland farmer who, when asked why he had left the city and returned to such poor land, set down his milk pail and in characteristic Danish fashion answered: "I'll have to think about that." I waited, standing in the manure, probably three or four minutes, while he conscientiously pondered the answer he should give. And he finally responded,

"Working in the city I was bored most of the time; farming is the most interesting job I know. Every day there are new problems to solve."

Another of the Jutland farmers, who had developed a comfortable living out of some of the worst land I saw in all my Danish travels, was a master carpenter and had, some twenty years before, worked in Copenhagen. When I asked him why he had returned to pioneer on the lonely Jutland heath, he answered that in Copenhagen he had been merely a number, whereas here he was a person. Actually, this particular individual was a good deal more since he had become one of the outstanding leaders in building up the local farm community.

None of these countries now feeds itself, if one takes into account the enormous imports that are needed of supplementary feeds, fertilizers, gasoline, machinery, etc. All of them must import other raw materials, especially Norway and Denmark. They live, very largely, by exporting products of the sea—the supply of which sometimes fails—of the forests, or processed raw materials.

One hears much criticism, difficult for a layman and foreigner to evaluate, of the management of Scandinavian forests. It is perfectly obvious that much potential forest land in south Sweden, for example, is not beginning to produce anything like the amount of wood that at one time it probably did; Norwegians have extensive plans for expanding their forests in the western part of the country. When it is remembered that half of Sweden's revenue comes from forests and forest products, the importance of these areas can be realized. Well-informed Swedes maintain that Sweden is not growing nearly as much timber as she cuts. They say that every acre of forest land in Sweden is mortgaged and that the interest payments must be met. They can be met only by overcutting.

Industrialization and urbanization are creating, inevitably, other difficulties. For example, with the development of central heating and the use of oil (which has to be imported) the demand for small trees formerly used for firewood has diminished so sharply that it is difficult to pay the cost of thinning the forests. A Japanese forester, traveling with a friend of mine, asked why thinning is not done more than one hundred meters from the highway. The high cost of the operation is part of the answer.

Although population has been growing slowly, it has been tending, as in so many other parts of the world, to form clots in metropolitan areas. This is, of course, creating many problems. In the mid-1950's a limnologist of the University of Lund stated that, provided the present development continued, Swedes will be forced to transform sewage into drinking water in order to save the water supply. This results in large part from the "rising standard of living," and the rapidly expanding use of flush toilets not only in new houses but in old. Another speaker at the same meeting, which took place at Kalmar, told of the necessity of closing bathing beaches because of an epidemic of paratyphoid.

In 1953, one of Sweden's leading child psychiatrists told me that many Swedes are highly insecure and compensate by exhibitionism. He gave as an instance of this the fact that in Stockholm enormous sums are spent on elaborate hospital structures—he mentioned one million kronor, or roughly $200,000, for a hall in a hospital—instead of trying to provide the maximum number of beds to meet desperate needs. He confirmed what I had been told by laymen, that doctors often have to falsify their diagnoses and present patients as more critically ill than they are to get them hospital beds.

And in spite of its low birth rates and the shift to the towns, even Scandinavia is not entirely free of the population problem. Erling Sveinbjørnsson, former Executive Director of the World Bank, recently wrote: "Some time ago a certain Danish newspaper stated that the Association of Danish Smallholders, as a reason for further splitting up the larger estates and establishing more small farms, pointed to the necessity of finding possibilities of employing the increasing population. From an economic point of view this does not seem like a feasible policy. . . . If the International Bank were asked, they probably would not lend money for such a purpose, as they are strongly in favor of more businesslike views . . . This seems to be an example showing that Scandinavia also has certain problems of overpopulation which perhaps might give rise to considerations concerning certain laws and regulations tending rather to increase the population than the opposite."

The population problem in Scandinavia is microscopic compared with that in most of the rest of the world and while these peaceful, cultured, civilized countries are not paradise, they certainly rear their peaks of well-being above a cloudy vastness of growing misery. Had their population grown for even a few decades at the rate that is typical of so much of the modern world, they too would be shadowed by the dark threat of disaster, with little hope of again rising into the sunlight.

These defects are minor, arising chiefly from the cultural changes implicit in a shift from a rural, agricultural society to urban industrialization, and are common to many parts of the world. They are insignificant, indeed, in relation to the over-all well-being of these people who, a hundred years ago, were nearly—if not quite—as poor as hundreds of millions in underdeveloped countries today. They were in a sense even poorer, since they had to labor hard to wrest a bare living from stubborn, rocky soils, often perched precariously between spring and fall. They had to struggle for food, for shelter, for warmth. At times their very survival was a triumph of skill and strength, character and wisdom.

They survived and built one of the best societies, measured by almost any reasonable criterion, that the world has yet seen. Out of poverty they created if not wealth, at least a way of living almost without poverty, as free from sickness as any modern society has ever been. While they suffer to some extent the penalties of relative overcrowding, and immoderate internal migration, they have long been wise enough to limit their numbers and avoid being swamped. This is, of course, not the only explanation of the success of their way of life. There is no doubt, however, that without birth control they would have been depressed not only to a miserable economic level, but to actual starvation.

A thoughtful Norwegian geologist summed up the philosophy behind the Scandinavian way of life by saying, "We have learned to live in our environment."

If the rest of the world would live by this precept the misery of hundreds of millions would disappear.

Are the rest of the people of the world less intelligent than these descendants of the pioneers who, only a few thousand years ago, pushed northward on the very heels of the retreating glaciers?

9

What Next?

IT SHOULD BE CLEAR THAT, UNLESS THERE IS A MARKED
change in course, we are drifting down a current that can
lead only to Maelström. To some readers it will seem I have
been unduly pessimistic. But men and women who have
worked in the field (as opposed to verbalizing in the library
and the office), especially in the backward countries, and who
are not constrained by their official positions, will, I think,
generally agree with me. Some, like Sir Charles Galton Darwin,[1] will even be so pessimistic as to conclude that disaster
is inescapable.

This conclusion I share, if we continue on our present inert
way.

Only one country faced with the problem of overpopulation is doing anything effective about it. India has made a
constructive but still quite inconclusive start. Pakistan has em-

barked on a program that may offer hope; it is too early to know. Japan has, thus far, made really significant progress.

The world—which includes nearly three billion individual people—is facing a difficult, and highly distasteful, situation.

It reminds me of a very polite small cousin who encountered his first oyster. His mother had said to him, "Clarence, you've never tasted an oyster. Here, try one." And with that she speared one from her own plate and popped it into his mouth.

Five minutes later she asked him, "How did you like the oyster, Clarence? Don't you want another one?"

To which he mumbled—his mouth still full of oyster—"I don't want this one."

Our mouth is full of unaccustomed oyster, but, like it or not, we've got to cope with it.

The problem is: How?

Obviously, birth control is not the sole answer to the population problem. As I pointed out in an earlier book (and as many other students of human ecology have also shown), there is need for a gargantuan expansion of improved land use, conservation of soil, water, forests and grasslands, industrialization, education, capital investment, technical assistance, and the rest of the constellation of programs that have so long and frequently been discussed, and so often badly applied. They must be far, far better done than heretofore. It is dubious whether many of these programs can be considered successful except the Marshall Plan and aid to Japan, both of them in areas well advanced in education, social organization, self-discipline, industrialization and business—and on the whole enjoying rather low birth rates. (It has been frequently pointed out that even in Marshall Plan countries, economic assistance has tended to exaggerate the disparity between the "haves" and the "have-nots," to a considerable extent because the "have-nots" overpopulate their own families, thus making them comparable to underdeveloped countries. And, of

course, it is not at all certain that some Marshall Plan countries have been kept out of the Communist camp more than
temporarily.)

The billions of dollars that have been spent in the underdeveloped countries have produced not much more than a
holding action. (Much of this expenditure has been for military aid, but this is such an elastic term that it is impossible to
sort it out in government reports.) In many cases, as in southeast Asia, more people are worse off today than they were before World War II; in others, despite the outpouring of cash,
more people are little if any better off—and living under a
threat of possible depression in their own or in the phil-
anthropic countries, and of the heightened pressures resulting
from a population growth that is more rapid every day. Millions of square miles of countryside (as in East Africa and
Latin America) are being downgraded under the twin impacts of technology and population demands. Millions are, today, more vulnerable to economic and social collapse than
ever before.

There are more hungry, more illiterate, more dissatisfied
people in the world today than ever before.

I have a favorite story I have told to many lecture audiences. It concerns a New England mental hospital with a
very small budget and a comparably small psychiatric staff.

There were no facilities for elaborate intake interviews, but
Yankee ingenuity devised a rough substitute.

New patients were put in a large room with concrete walls
and floors, and each was given a large mop. An attendant
would then turn on a big faucet and go out, closing the door
behind him.

The insane would go to work with the mops.

The sane would turn off the tap.

For years, now, as the flow of babies has grown greater
each year, the technicians—whether of the United Nations or

its associated organizations, the United States Government, or the Colombo plan—have been busy with their mops and constantly crying for bigger ones.

It is time, if not to turn off the tap, at least to cut down the flow as much as practicable, for at least a few years.

Probably the major obstacle in doing this (we must also recognize apathy, ignorance, the cake of custom, etc.) is the Roman Catholic Church. This organization, more than any other, has denied birth control to the world's people.

If, in this connection (and I must affirm great respect and admiration for much the Church does), I write with some intolerance, it is because I have seen what this particular defender of "the natural law" has done to men, women and children from New York to Latin America and Asia. *Family overpopulation* is probably the cause of more juvenile delinquency, poverty and general misery in the slums of New York, as well as other cities, than any other single factor. In the name of "the natural law," the Church has issued a ukase against doing anything effective to lower birth rates through the New York City Welfare Department where, according to staff members, they have been warned that they will be summarily discharged if they refer a worn-out mother to a Planned Parenthood center for help, whether on medical or psycho-economic grounds.

An even more indefensible example of the Church's attitude toward its people was shown, as has already been described, in the Haitian famine of 1959, in which two hundred Haitians were allowed to starve to death.

Perhaps we should not protest, in the name of outraged humanity, if the Church wanted to adopt this attitude only toward "its own." Religion, unless it be Communism, is generally assumed to be every man's private affair, even when inclusion in a faith is brought about by superstitious fear, by suppression of education and free speech. But is this a private

affair? Should we not reconsider our tolerance of religious
tyranny, and bring it into line with our attitude toward political tyranny?

What is very much in question, certainly, is the right of a
religious minority to drive its own beliefs and customs down
the throats of people outside its own organization.

Roman Catholics in the United States are constantly trying to force their own theology upon non-Catholic medical
practitioners, and they are supported in this effort by the
United States government. In scores of Roman Catholic hospitals across the land, theological, rather than scientific medical practice is required of staff doctors who may not perform
therapeutic abortions to save women's lives, nor prescribe
contraceptives in the interest of their health. This prohibition
applies to Protestant, Jewish, and non-believing doctors as
well as to Roman Catholics. The physicians frequently have
no choice; the Catholic hospital is the only one in the community. Either the doctor practices sectarian medicine, or he
has no hospital to which to take his patients. The money for
the construction and operation of these hospitals often comes
largely from an uninformed Protestant public; or, despite the
Constitutional separation of Church and State, from Federal
funds forcibly extracted by the tax collector.

The United States Public Health Service, which has charge
of disbursing such funds under the Hill-Burton Act, washes
its hands of the matter, and makes no requirement that hospitals be operated on medical rather than clerical standards. The
Service is far less concerned with providing treatment recommended by virtually all non-Catholic professors of obstetrics and gynecology in American medical schools than it
is in placating powerful Roman Catholic politicians who, in
this matter, represent a small minority. Up to the time this
book is written not a single Congressman or Senator has
shown himself willing to espouse medical principles endorsed by both the American Medical Association and the

American Public Health Association though there is much mouthing of words about "welfare" and even "peace through health." The Congressmen are not concerned with the health of American women!

The same situation obtains in the United Nations and its satellite organizations. Although Roman Catholics represent only about one-sixth of the world's people, they exercise an absolute veto in the U.N. and the World Health Organization. When a Norwegian delegate to the latter tried, a few years ago, simply to have a study made of the relationship between rapid population growth and public health, a small bloc that was almost entirely composed of countries dominated by the Roman Catholic Church threatened to withdraw if the study were undertaken. Here we had the ludicrous situation of Panama (pop. 800,000) outvoting India (pop. 400,000,000)! A similar situation occurred in the World Health Organization Assembly in May 1960. On both occasions U. S. delegates were, of course, on the side of expediency rather than of health.

In the U.N. it is difficult to assay the responsibility. The late Herschel Brickell, one of the first of America's Cultural Attachés, and a brilliantly successful one, used to maintain (privately) that the State Department had excellent brakes and reverse gears but no means of going forward. The U.N. is, of course, representative of eighty-odd State Departments. To make it responsive to the will of the world's people, rather than to that of the politicians and staff members who have a vested interest in the *status quo,* may be far more difficult than national reform.

When this writer, in 1949, published in the *Saturday Evening Post* a not unfriendly critique of President Truman's Point Four proposal—suggesting many of the difficulties that have subsequently developed, such as staffing problems, ingratitude among recipient peoples, widening of economic disparities as a result of American financing and technical aid, sharp population increases, etc.—he was told he could not write for general circulation and remain a member of the staff of the Organization of American States, which is a regional branch of the U.N. A bureaucrat, especially an international bureaucrat, is not supposed to express ideas, no matter how well founded they may be, if they are inconvenient!

I resigned from the O.A.S. If all U.N. employes who disagree with that body's do-nothing population policies were to resign, that organization would look as though it had been hit by a hurricane and be forced to face up to the perils of excessive population growth.

A change in American policy may confidently be expected despite the statement of Under Secretary of State Douglas Dillon who, in seeking $4,175,000,000 from the taxpayer for so-called foreign aid, categorically stated early in 1960 that any use of the funds to provide birth-control information was "completely out." [2] The great question is, Will the change come in time—or too late?

The most complete and representative study yet made of American families (unfortunately limited to white couples) showed that, "Attempts to avoid conception at some time are virtually universal among couples who have no fecundity impairment." [3] The drop in our birth rate during the depression of the thirties was evidence of the widespread acceptance and success of birth control.

There are many signs that the American people, almost pathologically good natured and willing to be pushed around, are getting fed up with minority dictation. Church group after church group, some preceding the action of the Lambeth Conference of the Anglican Communion, some following it, have expressed themselves in favor of birth control. In the State of Connecticut, clergymen have instituted suits, to be carried to the U. S. Supreme Court if necessary, challenging Comstock laws that make illegal the inclusion of birth control instruction in premarital counseling.

An admirable summary of the attitude of churches, including the Roman Catholic—that is to say, the expressed attitudes of theologians and clergymen—was published early in 1960.[4] This makes it clear that the Protestants, who outnumber even nominal Roman Catholics in the United States two-to-one, are taking a substantially united stand on the place of birth control as a part of religious ethics; and that they not only permit it but tend to make it a positive duty in Christian marriage. Jewish groups generally maintain their permissive stand; only the extreme conservatives are opposed to contraception.

Even the American Public Health Association has finally caught up with a pioneering public health nurse, Margaret Sanger, some thirty-two years after she organized the first international population conference in 1927, and declared for birth control as a public health measure. This follows, by many years, the teaching of birth control in virtually all non-Roman Catholic medical schools.

The blunder of the assembled Roman Catholic bishops in interjecting birth control as a possible instrument of our foreign policy, into the 1960 electoral campaign, drew blood; and unless one accepts the theory they were deliberately trying to "dump" Senator Kennedy, it must rank as the major political mistake the Church has made in this century. Much ingenuous tolerance of the Church's political machinations was swept away in the ensuing storm of controversy; and the possible effects of the candidates' religious beliefs and commitments on their presidential performance became more of an issue than they had been for thirty years. The Roman Catholic minority's effective veto on birth control is almost certainly coming to an end.

The Roman Catholic position on birth control is far from monolithic. The Vatican has been liberalizing the reasons justifying the use of the rhythm method at such a rate that parish priests are often well behind the Pope. A "liberal"

Catholic journal such as *Commonweal* will accept the right
of non-Catholics in our pluralistic society to use birth control, while Church powers in Connecticut and Massachusetts
follow what is essentially the old Anthony Comstock line.
(Comstock was, of course, a Protestant puritan of purest
ray serene.) It is reliably reported that the sale of contraceptives in these two states is as high, per capita, as in other
comparable areas. Professor Karl Sax has analyzed birth rates
in Massachusetts towns that are alleged to be predominantly
Roman Catholic and found them not to be significantly higher
than those of Protestant communities.[5] "Among fecund Catholic couples married at least ten years, 50 per cent have used
a method other than rhythm."[6] It would be more accurate,
perhaps, to state that 50 per cent *admitted* violating the
Church's precepts. How many others would have been reluc-
tant to make such an admission to a strange interviewer?

At birth control centers where the client's religion was
formerly recorded, the proportion of Catholics was usually
approximately the same as the proportion in the community
at large. Near the Mexican border, for example, it ran over
90 per cent.

With this minority Church group itself divided, with Protestant and Jewish leaders taking increasingly affirmative attitudes on birth control, and with the 30 to 40 per cent who
are un-churched in probable accord as to the desirability of its
use, the medieval-minded minority is in a position that is no
longer tenable. And there is evidence they know it.

For example, in the summer of 1958, a physician in a New
York City tax-supported hospital was ordered, by his Jewish
superior, to withhold standard contraceptive materials from
a diabetic, Protestant woman whose life, in the opinion of the
gynecologist, would have been endangered had she had another child. An enterprising reporter on the staff of the courageous *New York Post* broke the story, and such a storm of

indignation and community action blew up as the great and amorphous metropolis had not witnessed for decades.

Protestant, Jewish and civic organizations, with the support of the New York Academy of Medicine, and all professors of obstetrics and gynecology in the city's medical schools, together with support by the Planned Parenthood Federation of America, demanded that the unwritten law prohibiting contraception in city hospitals be rescinded. There was scarcely a day during the ensuing two months that newspaper stories, articles and editorials did not appear. Outstanding coverage and editorial support were given by the potent *New York Times*.

Throughout the two-month controversy the Roman Church was strangely inarticulate and unaggressive; and even in its statements it was divided. Ten years earlier City Hall would have been flooded with hundreds of thousands of letters written on order from the pulpit (as has been done before referenda in Masssachusetts and Connecticut) and the Knights of Columbus might well have picketed the Hospital Board en masse. In fact, statements from "The Power House," as Cardinal Spellman's office is known, seemed merely *pro forma*. The Chancellery could scarcely have said less.

The birth control advocates won in a shoo-in, when the Board of Hospitals met in September, and within forty-eight hours a clinic had been established in Bellevue Hospital. (The Roman Catholics received more magnanimous treatment than they had been giving—the Hospital Commissioner expressly excused from participation in the program "personnel who have religious or moral objections.")

It is well known that some leaders of Roman Catholic thought are deeply concerned by the population explosion, though their worries may not be mirrored in the allocutions of the Popes. It is possible they have confidence in making the rhythm method of birth control work. It is reported that the

Bishops were trying to head off a major birth control drive in the U.N. One may speculate they were dramatizing a reaffirmation for their wavering flock after an educational barrage from Sir Julian Huxley at a Planned Parenthood meeting, a *Life* magazine article, and especially after a major Columbia Broadcasting System telecast on the "population explosion."

For years it was impossible to find a Roman Catholic churchman to debate birth control on the radio or television. Reason, as well as the great weight of public opinion, is opposed to this refusal and the only defense they have for their position is *"Credo, ergo credo."* With millions of their own members rejecting this particular credulity, they are in an awkwardly untenable position.

The Protestants are, at last, not only asserting their rights, but making their weight felt in the way that Agnes Meyer urged in a speech to a Planned Parenthood group in 1956.

Speaking of the need to put the Planned Parenthood program on the same public health basis as tuberculosis control, she asked:

"Why, then, is it so difficult to achieve this? Why the taboo which surrounds the subject of birth control? Many public officials and medical men blame their fearful attitude on the Catholic Church. This is escapism. The Catholic Church has the right to defend and promulgate its ideas on birth control as much as any other group. Moreover, the Catholic Church is at least consistent in its attitude. If non-Catholics were as honest and forthright in advancing their theories, the influence of the Catholic Church would be confined to its own members and the fog of obscurity, vacillation and cowardice which surround the need for a nation-wide contraceptive program would be dissolved."

The minority position of the Catholics is at last being recognized and the majority opinion represented by organized Protestantism is being made so clear that even Congressmen and bureaucrats cannot much longer fail to get the point, especially as the American people become aroused enough to make their wishes known.

The end of the Roman Catholic ban—even the tacit ban—should have a widespread influence in hospitals, public health dispensaries and welfare departments. The health of American mothers and the well-being of children will be determined under the guidance of physicians instead of the dictation of priests. At last the wishes of the vast majority of Americans —90 per cent of fecund couples[7]—will prevail over the dogma of a minority.

There is considerable ground for hope that a more rational attitude may be developed toward birth control for poor people overseas. When President Eisenhower, an emotional man where religious matters are concerned, on the eve of a trip that included the Vatican, stipulated that it would be improper for our government to provide birth control to the people of other lands, even when requested by the governments concerned, he took the strange position that we should withhold from them what is standard medical practice in the United States. For decades, in "highly developed" countries in many parts of the world, birth control has been one of the privileges of the rich while, in the words of the song, the "poor get children"—and abortions.

Mr. Eisenhower gives the impression of being a reasonably humanitarian sort of man who would not withhold penicillin, vaccines, DDT or water purification. His decision to prohibit birth control—a decision in which, incidentally, he was not followed by Messrs. Stevenson, Humphrey, Symington, Nixon or Rockefeller—remains an unexplained mystery. But despite Eisenhower, with the emerging endorsement of birth control by groups representing the great majority of Americans, it is to be hoped backing will be given it in the World Health Organization and the United Nations.

Not only should we give birth-control help to any country receiving health or economic aid from us, we should encourage birth control in other countries as freely as we would currency reform, agricultural improvement, flood control, or emergency food supplies. Where there is no control of the birth rate and death rates are falling, we should not undertake any measure that would emphasize the disparity between these curves, unless we are willing to contribute the vast sums of money that may be needed to provide for the additional people.

Dr. Gerald Winfield, now of the International Cooperation Administration, suggested more than ten years ago in one of the best recent books on China, "All the proposed steps toward industrialization and increased agricultural productivity, all the processes necessary to enable China to play her logical role in a world community, all plans for her progress, are and will be futile unless her population growth can be controlled. . . . China is being so noisy about her purported economic growth that the public forgets the recurrent, regional famines that have taken place within the past half-decade.

"China can raise her standard of living only as she applies modern knowledge to the productive processes on the farm and in the factory to the advantage of a population that stays within quite definite limits. If, in modernizing, she also increases her population at a rate similar to that of Japan, ending up with as many people on the land as there are now, then there is little hope of raising the standard of living. . . .

"Three processes must be developed concurrently if the controlled decline of birth and death rates are to reach the levels noted: *existing checks on population growth must be left much as they are until positive means of reducing births are developed and practiced* [Italics added]; a medical-health program designed to bring about a rapid reduction in births to keep pace with declining deaths must be activated; the process of industrialization must be speeded so that natural restrictive factors, such as those which finally levelled off

Europe's population curve, will help limit the growth of population." [8]

We do not shrink from recommending changes in land inheritance and tenure, even when these may run counter to religious custom, if it seems necessary in improving agriculture, controlling erosion (though this was a special target of the Mau-Mau in Kenya), and making irrigation possible. We do not wait to be asked before giving help in improving diet. Hundreds of public health workers all over the world are trying to fight kwashiarkor.

When we make grants we presumably require adequate accounting to make sure the money is not stolen as happens in many countries where we have foreign aid programs. Why not, then, human accounting to insure that we do not build human populations into such liabilities that illiteracy and starvation are made an inescapable part of the future? Human beings are like water; they can be an asset or a destructive flood.

Our foreign aid efforts have, of course, been severely handicapped by lack of a clear over-all idea of what we are trying to do. Are we—as in the Near East and parts of Latin America —currying favor with the ruling oligarchies and dictators which are, for all practical purposes, the governments? (Our handouts to Perón, Somoza, Franco and Trujillo would seem to indicate this.) If we do not deal with the governments, how can we do anything for the people? When the government does not represent the people, but may even be bitterly hated by them, how does our own government resolve the dilemma? Do we not incur the hatred ourselves, when we bolster unpopular regimes?

When we give foreign aid are we trying to help the people as effectively as possible, or put on an advertising stunt to overshadow the Communists? And to overshadow the Communists in whose eyes? The reports that come back from Asia often make it seem as though our foreign policy were being written by Madison Avenue rather than by informed men concerned with the welfare of millions of people. Is foreign aid political or humanitarian? At times it may be both, but the two—as when we deny birth control facilities —may be mutually exclusive.

The advertising function has become so paramount during the past few years that what some people are beginning to call "pre-industrial" countries are using it as subtle blackmail. "Give us the aid," they demand. "You have no right to your luxurious existence while so many of our people are in misery." Some Asian officials to whom we have extended millions of dollars in aid, publicly criticize us because such a "small" proportion of the aid is made available for "development."

Other underdeveloped countries are beginning to go even further. They are saying, "Give us the money and let us decide how it shall be spent." In other words, give us a blank check, or we'll go to the bank across the street.

That hundreds of millions of dollars have been wasted, and many millions more stolen, is well known. In these ever-mounting demands—mounting because of growing populations—there could be a real threat to foreign aid programs. The resources of the American people—and their patience— are not, after all, inexhaustible.

As has been pointed out, despite the outpouring of billions of dollars, millions of people—especially in southeast Asia— are worse off than they were before World War II. And if many demographers, economists, agriculturists, public health experts, etc., are to be believed, they are going to be far worse off within the next decade or so.

The insane are still staying with their mops.

The realities of this situation would seem not only to justify but to dictate the inclusion of birth control in our foreign aid programs. We have been warned that to press birth control on any country would be politically disastrous. That I find hard to believe. The leaders of the emerging peoples are intelligent men and women. They have inherited from the past, as have we all, clichés, articles of faith, worn-out maps that do not fit 1960's territory. But learning the value of birth control is no more difficult than understanding the necessity of a currency that will be internationally acceptable, or of the need for large amounts of fertilizers for exhausted lands. In the long range, with few exceptions, it will be only those underdeveloped countries that have cut their birth rates that will escape misery and chaos. Are we to shy away from the idea, like an old maid from a mouse, and let our programs to help millions of people collapse in a smoking ruin? Such a process would seem, in its defeatist attitude, strangely un-American!

Should such aid be given only on a bi-lateral basis, or should it be included in United Nations technical assistance programs? The latter would have many advantages, but they would probably be outweighed by the disadvantages. Socioeconomic problems cannot be solved on a political basis. The realities of poor soil and maldistribution of rainfall will not bow to protocol. The way to meet needs is in accord with their magnitude and immediacy—not the kind of opportunism that is almost forced on the international bureaucrat. Roman Catholic threats and pressures are far more effective in a group obsessed with the idea of what "is not done" than in a group responsible to the people of the United States accustomed to "getting on with the job."

Dr. Richard Fagley has suggested the formation, within the United Nations, of a birth control bloc of nations wanting help with their population problems—perhaps in a sub-group such as W.H.O. or F.A.O. The idea has great merit, and were such a group formed, the United States could easily work with it. India and Pakistan would seem the natural leaders of such a movement within the United Nations.

That the American people should help provide birth control to any country requesting it, and that it should inspire the acceptance of such a health measure just as it does malaria and yaws control, or BCG inoculation against tuberculosis, would seem obvious except to the Roman Catholic minority. But that this small group should have the controlling voice in setting national policy is, of course, indefensible nonsense.

That the ideas of this same minority should determine U.N. policy is quite as unreasonable. If the policies of W.H.O., UNICEF and other U.N. bodies continue to follow this minority line, we Americans would be quite justified in withdrawing our financial support.

We have seen how a Presbyterian President has agreed with Roman Catholic policy for his government and there is much evidence that many American people are also aware of the hazard of a Roman Catholic successor in 1960, either as President or Vice-President. So critical is the threat of population growth that a candidate's unwillingness (no matter what his religion) to try to cope with it should be sufficient grounds for disqualifying him. This should be true no matter how able he might otherwise be, since our foreign policy, the hope of raising world living standards, and peace itself, are placed in jeopardy by such denial.

A president who ignored the danger of nuclear warfare would, on this score alone, be disqualified. It is high time that everyone, from President Eisenhower and Pope John down to the humblest, needy mother, recognize that birth control is no longer "controversial." What is controversial is opposition to it, and that on the part of a minority. Without birth control the world cannot possibly escape disaster.

The population explosion is both more dangerous and more immediate than the H-bomb.

The population explosion has already been triggered off.

What are the possiblilities of again getting it under control?

Given an unobstructed will, free of Roman Catholic opposition, with supporting funds amounting to a mere fraction of what is now being spent on space exploration, the possibilities are considerable.

In all areas of high living standards, chiefly Western Europe, North America, Japan and Oceania, the small family pattern is now generally accepted. The small family, democracy and high living standards, in this twentieth century go hand in hand.

The U.S.S.R. has recently legalized easy abortion and, it is reported, is developing a birth-control program as a means of abortion control. Both the Communist Chinese and the Indian governments, under whom live more than a third of the world's people, sponsor birth control, though the latter government is pushing it—or at least talking about it—more than the former. Pakistan and Egypt, with a combined population of more than one hundred million, also have government-sponsored programs. Thus, well over half the world is either technically promoting birth control, or it is included as an intrinsic part of its folkways.

Scores of millions of men and women in other parts of the world would readily accept birth control were it available.

In most societies (perhaps excluding Africa and some Muslims) the better educated and more prosperous groups have adopted birth control; their example is important. Numerous surveys, in many countries, have elicited the information that most parents want only three or four children. The greater the life expectancy, and the more likelihood that the children will be an economic burden, the greater seems to be the desire for smaller families.

The difference between what parents say they want, and the way they act, will often vary considerably. But it would probably not be unduly optimistic to assume that, were acceptable contraceptives cheap and available, at least half the families in the world would make an effort to limit the size of their families. That they might overdo this—the bugbear of "race suicide"—is not likely to be considered seriously by anyone who knows how anxious most women are to have children. Those who, through genetically determined attitudes (if these exist), or through conditioning, choose to have no children would, of course, be eliminated in a single generation and, thus, could not have more than a limited and temporary influence.

There is an additional large segment of the population that, with education, could fairly easily be shown the advantages of the small family. (The large family also has advantages, under many circumstances, but as we face absolute overpopulation these must, inevitably, be set aside.)

The Japanese, with government subventions, a tradition of the limited family, going back three or four hundred years, and adequate medical resources, cut their birth rate by an astounding 50 per cent in ten years. It is not to be expected that the rest of the world would equal this performance, especially since the Japanese acceptance of abortion is most unusual; but a marked downturn in the birth rates of from 50 to 65 per cent of the world's families—perhaps more—might be expected within ten years, given favorable conditions. (This is admittedly a "guess-timate" but it is based on a first hand knowledge of conditions on four continents, and considerable reading.)

There has developed, during the past decade, a widespread feeling, even among those who work in the birth control field, that we cannot look for much success in checking population growth until we have a much simpler means of control, preferably an inexpensive pill to be taken by mouth—some means of prevention that is separated from the act of coitus. That this will be enormously helpful is unquestionable. But that we must wait for "the pill" is dubious.

Birth control began to take hold in the British Isles when they were still, medically, about as underdeveloped as are Mexico and Egypt today. Even more significant is what happened in Scandinavia from which there are fairly reliable statistics going back to 1721.[9] "The birth rate showed a downward trend from the middle of the eighteenth century . . .

until about 1840, when it rose for some two decades before embarking on the long-term decline which extended into our present century." [10] This author suggests that "birth control must have been fairly widely practised even in those early days." [11] This view is shared by another Scandinavian population student who writes: "It seems very probable that in Eastern Sweden some form of birth control was practiced. The difference between the drop in the birth figures in different parts of the country following the crop failures of 1771-72 strengthens such suspicions . . . the decline was as great as 47.9 per cent in the county of Blekinge, 46.8 per cent in the county of Jönköping, and 56.3 per cent in the county of Kalmar." [12]

This was, of course, long before the days of modern contraceptives—even such simple methods as foam tablets, suppositories and condoms—and the method used by the Swedish peasants was probably *coitus interruptus*. The fact that this took place in *pre-industrial* Sweden, where the majority of people lived by subsistence agriculture, makes the situation even more closely analogous to that in the underdeveloped world today. Unless we are willing to concede superior intelligence on the part of the Swedes, there seems to be no reason why we should not expect comparably intelligent behavior from the Indians and some other peoples. (The absence of certain Christian attitudes toward sex, that tend to equate it with "sin" and guilt, will be of inestimable help in much of Asia.)

While a pill that could be taken by mouth once a month, or soon after intercourse, or an inoculation that could be taken once a year, might speed up the acceptance and effectiveness of birth control, no such substance of proven reliability is known to exist. There is some hopeful activity in scientific laboratories but several years may well elapse before a satisfactory physiological means of conception control is available —and only then, in all probability, if there is a great expansion

of research. The one group of compounds of proven effectiveness must be ingested about twenty days out of every month,
at a cost of about ten dollars.

There is, however, such a widespread desire to limit families
that such simple contraceptives as are now available would
probably be highly acceptable to most people.

Parenthetically, two other means of conception control
should be mentioned, leaving aside frequent abortions as
ethically unacceptable and physically damaging, though
many millions are undoubtedly performed every year. (It is
believed, by doctors in as good a position as anyone to know,
that for every live birth in France there are one or more abortions; the low birth rate in Uruguay, in many ways the most
progressive country in South America, is attributed to the
same cause. Abortions in Japan have been estimated as high
as two million a year—falling since the organization of a
chain of birth control clinics—and the number performed
in the United States may not be far from a million. An estimate
of ten million abortions a year, in a world with one hundred million births, is probably conservative. The number of
women dying after induced abortion, especially in countries
without adequate medical services, undoubtedly runs into
many thousands—which ought to be a further burden on the
conscience of those who deny the world's poor the blessing
of contraception.)

In some areas, where medical services are available, sterilization—both male and female—is increasingly sought. It
has been estimated, for example, that in Puerto Rico one
woman out of every six, in the child-bearing age, has been
sterilized. (In the island *la operación* has achieved some status
as a political favor comparable to that which the bag of coal
once had in the Tammany district leader's office.) Sterilizations are usually performed after women have had large
families and, thus, do little to reduce rate of population
growth. In India, in some of the more prosperous states, men

who are willing are actually paid to be sterilized. In the aggregate, however, it is unlikely that sterilizations can be performed frequently enough to reduce population pressures on a large scale, though at the family level they may be a godsend. Since they are usually permanent—irreversible—they are not to be undertaken lightly. On the other hand, legal or medical proscription of sterilization until women have had four, or six, or even more, children, seems indefensible. If the State—or the medical profession—has no right to force contraception (or sterilization) on a woman, it certainly has no right to deny it.

One of the most radical suggestions as to fertility control came from Dr. Homi Bhabha, President of the Indian Atomic Energy Commission, at the 1959 meeting in New Delhi of the International Planned Parenthood Federation.

What India needs, said Dr. Bhabha in effect, is not the perfect contraceptive but something that will reduce overall fertility. If the Indian birth rate could be cut 30 per cent, economic development could overtake population growth and we could raise our standard of living.

What we need, he concluded, is an anti-fertility agent to be added to the rice, grain or salt, that would cut our birth rate by this amount.

Without accepting Dr. Bhabha's economic estimate, or even the paramountcy of the economic factor, there is no denying the ingeniousness of his idea, could it be made acceptable to the salt users. The fact that it would influence the fertility of the entire population, across the board, would make it more acceptable by making it non-discriminatory. Prime minister and peasant would be influenced, alike. It would, assuredly, have to reduce fecundity without cutting libido, or barricades would rise in the streets. (The problem of making an oral contraceptive acceptable would be solved easily if to it there could be added a mild aphrodisiac.) By acting independently of the momentary impulses of the man or woman, it would, of course, have an enormous advantage over most current contraceptive measures.

As a means of protecting the mother from child-bearing that because of multi-parity or other damaging effects upon her health would make pregnancy really dangerous, it would of course be quite unsatisfactory. For this we need a contraceptive with a success rate as near 100 per cent as possible.

With the Bhabha balm, the oral contraceptive and mass sterilization unavailable, what can be done to halt the population runaway within the next ten years?

Given the history of falling birth rates in other parts of the world, even in pre-industrial societies, and given reasonably effective simple contraceptives, there is little justification for complete discouragement.

There are available vaginal foam tablets that, while apparently not so reliable as the somewhat complicated diaphragm and jelly method recommended by most American gynecologists, are fairly effective. New non-foaming tablets promise well but clinical proof has not yet been published. The cheapest contraceptive, an aerosol developed by a St. Louis philanthropist, is also reported to be highly efficacious though at this writing only preliminary tests have been made. Its application is as simple as squirting shaving cream onto one's face; in fact, the shaving cream "bomb" inspired the invention. Each application is said to cost about two cents.

The most widely used contraceptive in America, and perhaps in the world, is the condom. While the manufacturer's and pharmacist's markup make it as expensive as most drugs and medical appliances in the United States, it can be manufactured cheaply enough so that it would be practicable for many large areas in underdeveloped countries, even with those having as low per capita incomes as India where a condom factory could be set up and workers trained for around $500,000. Even if American funds were not available for the establishment of such factories, it is difficult to understand why they should not be built by would-be developing countries. The cost of preventing the birth of a child is a tiny fraction of the cost of rearing and educating him, and providing a job as he grows up. This is especially true in countries where there are great pools of illiteracy and unemployment.

The availability of hundreds of millions of contraceptives, either at a nominal, subsidized figure, or free of cost, would almost certainly result in widespread use. The improved living standards that would result from smaller families should prove the most effective education on the advantages of birth control.

There has been serious discussion in both Japan and India of using tax laws to discourage large families—to impose progressively heavier taxes on every family with the arrival of the third, fourth and fifth child, up to the limit.

The value of this when the underdeveloped countries can provide contraceptives should be obvious. Indeed, it might well be seriously considered for such a country as the United States, as a means of regulating growth. Inflation has been necessary here, in part to finance our baby boom. Governmental costs, especially at the local and state levels, are increasing in large part because of population growth. The tiny increments of take-home pay, as has been pointed out, are whittled down because they must be distributed among more people.

Many of our worst headaches in the next thirty or forty years—growing need for hospitals, schools, highways, water supplies, welfare benefits, space (in parks, etc.), new jobs at the rate of 1.3 to 1.5 million a year, pollution control, etc.—could be assuaged with a reduction in our birth rate. And if this is to stay high, on whom should the burden fall if not on the parents? (There is, of course, little excuse for having an unwanted child in the United States.)

It is hardly likely that such an intelligent approach to our own population trend will be developed within this century. (Conservation commissions across the land have been vainly trying for twenty years to cut back our white-tailed deer numbers by having does shot along with bucks. When we shy away from a realistic approach to the population problem in deer there's little likelihood that we shall face it in the human species. Not, of course, that I am suggesting drowning babies —even girl babies!) The Japanese and the Indians are years ahead of us in understanding population phenomena and the need for a population policy. We shall probably have to learn the necessity of a population policy, from them, in the twenty-first century.

It is objected by some population students that while death rates are high in underdeveloped countries families will want many children to insure their perpetuation. There is much truth in this contention but it should be remembered that populations are growing primarily because death rates are falling. Furthermore, in the smaller families, the life expectancy of the mother—and therefore the care of the family and the children—will improve. The willingness to use contraceptives after the birth of the third or fourth child may be expected to grow. (The ethics of breeding slave labor to support one's later years have already been commented on.)

The next three or four decades are likely to prove critical. Unless population growth can be significantly reduced within that period, a number of countries and, indeed, entire regions, will probably not be able to pull back from disaster. Economic, political and cultural development will not be able to keep up with the rising demand. The population wave will rise until it breaks in famine, revolution, perhaps spilling across international borders in what may be local wars, or which may become general wars.

The danger is very great that China will move southward into about the only part of Asia with surplus food, unless she decides to move west. The latter seems unlikely unless she should achieve the impossible by industrial development fast enough to match the logistics of the U. S. S. R.

The starvation that has already hit Haiti may be expected to spill over into other Latin American areas and, very likely, many parts of Africa. Not even all the billions we may be able to pour out can—it seems probable—avert such disasters. The population wave will recede. Whether it ever rises again will depend on the character of the reversal.

Whatever that may be, the price in human misery will be horrible. Whether we, of the temporarily prosperous West, can escape being caught in the backwash, will depend on many and unpredictable factors.

That we are morally involved is widely agreed, and that we have a responsibility to help the underdeveloped nations. What is not generally recognized is that we also have a responsibility to set an example.

With something like one-sixteenth of the world's population, we are using more than one-half of the world's raw material. We get it simply because what we have to barter the poor countries desperately need.

Is this morally defensible?

The raw materials we are buying today—the iron ore, non-ferrous metals, oil, topsoil—may be a matter of life and death twenty or thirty years hence, if these poor countries have been able to develop and to escape famine. By then, many of them will have doubled populations. Can we defend the right to deprive tomorrow's child?

Many leaders in the West, though still not enough, have begun to recognize and recommend the necessity of cutting birth rates. Yet ours, in the United States remains relatively high. Our population is doubling at about the same speed as that of India.

Does there not lie upon us the categorical imperative to act as we urge others to act? In a world that is being swamped by people, do we have any right to increase the human cargo? Should we not as a matter of principle and example limit our reproduction to replacement, or even a little less?

These are not easy questions, nor are we likely to find simple answers. But there is no rug under which we can sweep the questions. They are with us now and they will be even more omnipresent tomorrow. Every one of us should go back to pulse-counting, as a reminder of what is happening, as a sort of population rosary.

One . . . two . . . three . . .

For every hundred beats, *more* than a hundred more people in the world . . . every hour . . . every day . . . every week . . . every month . . . inexorably, relentlessly, while we work, eat, play, make love, sleep—for every hundred pulse beats, more than a hundred more hungry, ignorant, desperate people.

Tranquilizers may quiet the insane, dissolve their dreams and their fears. But these are not dreams. There are almost 100 more people a minute, 6,000 the hour, 140,000 the day, 50,-000,000 the year! They cannot be wished out of the world. They must be lived with.

And by the time our children are middle-aged, there may be twice as many of them—perhaps increasing even faster. Not nearly enough is being done to provide for them. It is doubtful whether it is humanly possible to do enough to satisfy them. Almost nothing is being done to help them control their numbers.

And time is running out.

Almost one hundred more every minute . . .

Appendix

Several private organizations have, for a number of years, concerned themselves with population and other problems, such as maternal health, that, in one way or another, involve birth control. They are especially important in the United States, where government assistance to such programs is limited. Seven southeastern states include birth control in their public-health activities, but their effectiveness varies largely with the personal interest of the public-health officers involved—and with their concern, or lack of it, with the possibility of criticism. Smaller units such as municipal hospitals are slowly, though increasingly, including contraceptive service as part of normal services, especially in connection with *post partum* care.

Simple contraceptives, many of which unfortunately are still not of clinically proven reliability, are widely sold in drugstores and, in some places, even supermarkets. The poor and the uninformed—those of our people who most need contraceptive help—are still least likely to receive it. The well-off and the educated have little difficulty even in Massachusetts and Connecticut, the only two states where birth-control provision or use remains illegal.

The Planned Parenthood Federation of America, 501 Madison Avenue, New York City 22, has for nearly forty years, through its affiliates—now numbering about one hundred—provided birth-control services in its own medically supervised centers, from coast to coast. It also helps, with medical care, subfertile couples to have children that might otherwise not be conceived. In scores of communities it provides facilities for pre-marital education.

The Federation was a pioneer in fostering research on the physiology of human reproduction, through grants to scientists, a program that has now been assumed by foundations, the National Institutes of Health, etc. Its research is currently concentrated on social aspects of family planning (including motivational and psychological) and the clinical evaluation of contraceptives, for which it has unique facilities.

The Federation has also, through its information and education programs, been a principal source of information for the general public on population, birth control and related subjects; its pamphlets, articles, news releases, etc., reach an American readership of several hundred million a year.

The Federation and its affiliates are supported entirely by privately contributed funds.

The Population Reference Bureau, 1507 M Street, N.W., Washington 5, D.C., is another private organization in this field, also financed by individual and foundation contributions, but its purpose is entirely educational. Through its authoritative *Population Bulletin*, news releases, and the direct provision of information on population to newspapers, broadcasting stations, etc., it has been an effective and continuing educational force that reaches millions of people not only in the United States, but also in other parts of the world where its material is receiving growing acceptance by the press.

The Population Council, 230 Park Avenue, New York City, also a private organization, is entirely supported by foundation funds and those of large donors. It is concerned with research (both by its own staff and through grants-in-aid) and with technical, professional education of physicians, biologists, demographers and others at professional or policy-making levels.

Its programs are being carried out both in the United States and abroad.

The International Planned Parenthood Federation, 69 Eccleston Square, London, S.W.1, is a federation of some thirty family-planning organizations, of which the Planned Parenthood Federation of America is one. Its program is, on a small scale, in general comparable to that of the American Federation. It is the web that ties together birth-control organizations all over the world. A few of its members are governmental, and many affiliates receive some support from their respective governments. The IPPF is supported by membership dues and by private contributions, chiefly from the United Kingdom and the United States. *The World Population Emergency Campaign*, with an American office at 51 West 42nd Street, New York City, is currently (1960) seeking additional funds for the IPPF.

References

CHAPTER 2

[1] *The Economist* (London), February 6, 1960.

CHAPTER 3

[1] Elton, Charles S. *Voles, Mice and Lemmings; Problems in Population Dynamics.* New York: Oxford University Press, 1942.
Lack, David L. *The Natural Regulation of Animal Numbers.* London: Oxford University Press, 1954.

[2] Christian, John J. A Review of the Endocrine Responses in Rats and Mice to Increasing Population Size Including Delayed Effects on Offspring, 1957. *Lectures and Review Series.* Bethesda, Md.: Naval Medical Research Institute.

[3] Darlington, C. D. *Darwin's Place in History.* Oxford: Blackwell, 1959, p. 45. Prof. Darlington of Oxford puts the estimate at 50,000 generations.

[4] Vogt, William. *Road to Survival.* New York: William Sloane Associates, 1948, p. 77.

[5] *U. N. Statistical Yearbook.* New York: Columbia University Press, 1958, p. 43.

[6] Gregg, Alan. "A Medical Aspect of the Population Problem," *Science* (Washington) CXXI, 1955, p. 682.

[7] Brown, Harrison. Speech to the Planned Parenthood Federation of America, November 19, 1958.

[8] Mukerjee, Dr. Radhakamal. Proceedings of the Sixth International

Conference, International Planned Parenthood Federation, pp. 31, 32.

9 De Martini, Rev. Raymond. *The Right of Nations to Expand by Conquest.* Washington: The Catholic University of America Press, 1947. Reprinted 1955. *x* + 174 pp.

CHAPTER 4

1 Hitchcock, S. T. Highway Traffic and Traffic Fatalities in 1975 in *Applications of Demography*, Scripps Foundation and University of Chicago Population Research and Training Center, 1957, p. 82.

2 *World Health*, January-February 1958, p. 11.

3 Sears, Paul B. "The Inexorable Problem of Space," *Science* (Washington), CXXVII, No. 3288, January 3, 1958, p. 13.

4 Billings, C. H. "Drought Problems and Their Effect on Municipal Water Supplies," *American Journal of Public Health* (April, 1955), pp. 472-473.

5 *Science News Letter*, August 1, 1959, p. 70.

6 Borgström, Georg. "Le dilemme de la technique moderne," *Revue de la Société Belge d'Études et d'Expansion* (Liège), 1958, p. 8.

7 *U. N. Statistical Yearbook.* New York: Columbia University Press, 1958, p. 37.

8 Durand, Loyal, Jr. in *Focus*, New York: American Geographical Society, May, 1959, p. 6.

9 Bogue, Donald J. in *Wall Street Journal*, September 17, 1959.

10 Reston, James, *New York Times*, March 25, 1960, p. 26.

11 *Science News Letter*, 77, 9, February 27, 1960, p. 133.

12 *New York Times*, August 9, 1959.

13 Letter to the *Wall Street Journal*, March 1, 1960.

CHAPTER 5

[1] "World Population and Resources." Political and Economic Planning: London, 1955, p. 18.

[2] "The Price of Unclean Air," *The UNESCO Courier* (New York), March, 1959, p. 11.

[3] *Atlantic Monthly*, May, 1959.

[4] *The Economist*, (London), July 6, 1957, p. 27.

[5] *Economic Bulletin for Asia and the Far East*, X, No. 1, June, 1959, pp. 4, 29.

[6] *The Economist* (London), December 13, 1958, p. 16.

[7] Leakey, L. S. B. *Defeating Mau Mau*. London: Methuen & Co., Ltd., 1954, pp. 62, 63.

[8] Ibid., p. 135.

[9] Ibid., p. 144.

[10] "The African Revolution," *The Economist* (London) December 13, 1958, p. 19.

[11] *World Illiteracy at Mid-Century*, UNESCO, 1957, p. 52.

[12] Kimble, George, H. T. "Ghana," *Focus*. New York: American Geographical Society, April, 1959.

[13] *New York Times*, March 15, 1959, p. 10.

[14] Ibid.

[15] *New York Times*, December 7, 1958.

[16] *World Illiteracy at Mid-Century*, UNESCO, 1957, p. 50.

[17] de Castro, Josué. *The Geography of Hunger*. Boston: Little, Brown & Co., 1952.

[18] Ibid., p. 72.

[19] Luitss, N. G. W. "World Markets for Synthetic Detergents." Shell Petroleum Co., Ltd., Chemical Industry Administration, London.

[20] Kamat, Melba, and R. G. Kamat. *Diet and Fecundity in India.* Proceedings, Sixth International Conference on Planned Parenthood, London, 1960, p. 118.

[21] *Harper's Magazine* (New York), January 1953.

[22] *The Economist* (London), December 10, 1955.

[23] Senior, Clarence. "Demography and Economic Development," *Social and Economic Studies* (Jamaica, W. I.), VII, No. 3, September, 1958, p. 12.

[24] *New York Herald Tribune*, May 31, 1955.

[25] Ward, R. Gerard. "The Population of Fiji," *Geographical Review* (New York), XLIX (July 3, 1959), p. 341.

[6] Kawasaki, Ichiro. *The Japanese Are Like That.* Rutland, Vt.: Chas. E. Tuttle Co., 1955.

[27] Ibid., p. 138.

[28] Ibid., p. 196.

[29] Ibid., p. 149.

[30] Ibid., p. 217.

[31] Green, Martin. "A Mirror for Anglo-Saxons," *Harper's Magazine* (New York) CCXIX, No. 1311, August, 1959, p. 36.

[32] *The Economist* (London), April 18, 1959, p. 209.

CHAPTER 6

[1] *Report on India's Food Crisis and Steps to Meet It,* by The Agricultural Production Team. Sponsored by Ford Foundation, 1959, p. 22. Issued by the government of India.

[2] Ibid., p. 3.

[3] Ibid., p. 1.

[4] Planned Parenthood. Bombay, India, January-February, 1960, p. 1.

[5] *Ford Report*, p. 11.

[6] Ibid., p. 13.

[7] Ibid., p. 14.

[8] *New York Times*, July 15, 1959.

[9] *Ford Report*, p. 145.

[10] Ibid., p. 146.

[11] Coale, Ansley, J., and Edgar M. Hoover. *Population Growth and Economic Development in Low-Income Countries*. Princeton: Princeton University Press, 1958, p. 100.

[12] Ibid., p. 11.

[13] As this book goes to press, we receive reports that the Indian Government Planning Commission has recommended the expenditure, during the Third, Five-Year Plan, of $210,000,000 on birth control and that it actually hopes one-fifth or one-sixth of this amount will be available.

[14] *Saturday Evening Post*, September 19, 1959, p. 53.

[15] Gille, Halvor. *The Demographic History of the Northern European Countries in the Eighteenth Century*. Population Studies, III, June 1, 1949. Population Investigation Committee, London School of Economics.

[16] U. S. Foreign Aid. Eighty-sixth Congress, first session. House Document 116, Washington, 1959, p. 41.

CHAPTER 7

[1] Freedman, Ronald, P. K. Whelpton and A. A. Campbell. *Family Planning, Sterility and Population Growth*. New York: McGraw-Hill, 1959, pp. 17, 77.

[2] Ibid., p. 296.

[3] Flugel, J. C. *Men and Their Motives.* New York: International Universities Press, 1947, p. 25.

[4] Brody, Samuel. *Facts, Fables and Fallacies on Feeding the World Population.* Federation Proceedings, 11, September 3, 1952, p. 681.

[5] Hauser, Philip, M. (Ed.) *Population and World Politics.* Glencoe, Ill.: The Free Press, 1958, p. 30.

[6] Flugel, op. cit., pp. 8-35.

[7] Ibid., p. 9.

[8] Brown, Harrison S. *Challenge of Man's Future.* New York: Viking Press, 1954.

[9] Darwin, Sir Charles Galton. *The Next Million Years.* New York: Doubleday & Co., 1952.

[10] *New York Herald Tribune*, January 12, 1959.

[11] *Manchester Guardian*, September 4, 1959.

CHAPTER 8

[1] Kraabe, Ludwig. *Histoire de Danemark.* Copenhagen: Munksgaard, 1950, p. 16.

[2] Larsen, Karen. *A History of Norway.* Princeton: Princeton University Press, 1948, p. 8. Published for the American-Scandinavian Foundation.

[3] Nuttonson, M. Y. *Agricultural Climatology of Sweden.* Washington: The American Institute of Crop Ecology, 1950, p. 17.

[4] Ibid.

[5] An excellent brief history of the co-operative movement in Denmark was published by *Det Danske Selskab* in 1947.

[6] Strøm, Wilh. De Norske Bygdealmenninger. Saertrykk av Tidsskrift for Skogbruk. Oslo, 1, 1942, p. 1.

[7] Haden-Guest, Stephen, John K. Wright and Arlene M. Teclaff, editors. *A World Geography of Forest Resources.* New York: The Ronald Press, 1956.

[8] Nelson, George R. (ed.) *Freedom and Welfare: Social Patterns in the Northern Countries.* 1953. p. 320.

[9] The quotations from Almqvist are adapted from a translation kindly made for me by Hélène Hertzberg.

[10] Leach, Henry Goddard. (ed.). *A Pageant of Old Scandinavia.* Princeton: Princeton University Press, 1946, p. 313. Published for the American-Scandinavian Foundation, New York.

CHAPTER 9

[1] Darwin, Sir Charles Galton. *The Next Million Years.* New York: Doubleday & Co., 1952.

[2] *New York Times,* February 19, 1960, p. 1.

[3] Freedman, Ronald, P. K. Whelpton and A. A. Campbell. *Family Planning, Sterility and Population Growth.* New York: McGraw-Hill, 1959, p. 61.

[4] Fagley, Richard M. *The Population Explosion and Christian Responsibility.* New York: Oxford University Press, 1960.

[5] Sax, Karl. *Standing Room Only.* Boston: Beacon Press, 1955, p. 184.

[6] Freedman, Whelpton, Campbell, op. cit., p. 183.

[7] Freedman, Whelpton, Campbell, op. cit., p. 61.

[8] Winfield, Gerald. *China: The Land and the People.* New York: William Sloane Associates, 1948, pp. 334-40.

[9] Gille, Halvor. "The Demographic History of the Northern European Countries in the Eighteenth Century," *Population Studies* (London), III, No. 1, June, 1949, p. 3.

[10] Ibid., p. 54.

[11] Ibid., p. 39.

[12] Utterström, Gustaf. "Some Population Problems in Pre-Industrial Sweden," *The Scandinavian Economic History Review* (Uppsala, Sweden) II No. 2, 1954, p. 159.

Index

abortion, world figures, 228; *see also* country references

Africa, American development of mines, 80; birth control, 95, 126; climate, 177; compared with cultural and scientific accomplishments of Scandinavia, 194; cultures based on low population densities, 94; education, 98 ff.; famine, 126; food production, 90, 94 ff.; highway system, 99; ignorance, 97 ff.; illiteracy, 90; impact of European rule on land/population equation, 94; increased cattle production through predator control, 96; lack of trained technicians and specialists, 98; languages, 99 ff.; Mau Mau revolt and overpopulation, 94 ff.; of mid-twentieth century, 100; nationalism and racism, 96 ff.; overgrazing, 95 ff.; political corruption in new states, 99; population figures, 90, 94 ff., 98 ff.; resources, 98; rulers' lack of knowledge of tropical environment, 96; similarity to El Salvador, 101; social services, 98 ff.; standard of living, 97 ff.; wildlife, 30, 70; *see also* underdeveloped countries

A.F.L.-C.I.O., 81

agricultural revolution, 43 ff.

Alaska, climate, 178; cost of new political situation, 72; hunting and fishing, 70

American Museum of Natural History, 68

American Public Health Association, birth control policy, 215

American taxpayer, 32 ff.; cost of foreign aid to underdeveloped and overpopulated countries, 167 ff.; cost of indigent families, 72 ff., 75, 165; cost of juvenile delinquency, 78; cost of subsidization, 71; featherbedders, 71; tax supported hospitals, 212 ff.

anti-fertility agent, 229 ff.

Antigua, decrease in death rates, 46

Arab refugees, population figures, 112

Argentina, daily consumption of animal proteins, and birth rate, 106 ff.; foreign aid, 31; soap consumption per capita, 108; *see also* Latin America

art museums, in United States, 67 ff.

Asia, destruction of wildlife, 30, 70; food production, 90 ff.; illiteracy, 90; Point Four program, 10 ff.; population figures, 90; population policy, 17; starvation, 92 ff.; *see also* country references, *and* ECAFE region

atomic energy, 62 ff.

Australia, daily consumption of animal protein, and birth rates, 107; population increase, 16; soap consumption per capita, 108

Barbados, decrease in death rates, 46; education, 105; population density,